Healthy Choices

W9-CHQ-749

Grades 6–8

A Positive Approach to Healthy Living
- Self-management
- Diet
- Exercise

Published by World Teachers Press®
www.worldteacherspress.com

Published with the permission of R.I.C. Publications Pty. Ltd.

Copyright © 2006 by Didax, Inc., Rowley, MA 01969. All rights reserved.

First published by R.I.C. Publications Pty. Ltd., Perth, Western Australia. Revised by Didax Educational Resources.

Printed in the United States of America.

Order Number 2-5255
ISBN 1-58324-232-5

A B C D E F 10 09 08 07 06

395 Main Street
Rowley, MA 01969
www.worldteacherspress.com

HEALTHY CHOICES

Foreword

Living in a modern technological society can have detrimental effects on our health. On average, we are less active and consume far more fast food than is recommended by health experts. These kinds of habits are causing health problems like obesity and diabetes to develop much earlier in life than ever before. It is up to adults to guide and encourage children to live in a healthy way.

Healthy Choices, 6–8 aims to increase students' awareness of healthy lifestyles, helping them to develop positive habits that will stay with them into adulthood.

The book is divided into four sections:

- A Healthy Lifestyle
- A Healthy Diet
- Exercise and Fitness
- Self-Management

Other titles in this series are:

- *Healthy Choices, 1–3*
- *Healthy Choices, 4–5*

Contents

Healthy Choices is divided into four sections –

* **A *Healthy Lifestyle*** focuses on the benefits of a healthy lifestyle and the effects of unhealthy habits.

* **A *Healthy Diet*** focuses on the benefits of good nutrition and the problems with junk food.

* ***Exercise and Fitness*** focuses on the benefits of physical activity and how everyone can keep fit.

* ***Self-Management*** focuses on how we can make healthy choices for ourselves to increase our general well-being and self-esteem.

Teacher Page

A teacher page accompanies each student worksheet. It provides the following information:

The title shows the particular activity from the section being covered.

The subtitle shows which of the four sections of the book is being covered.

Specific indicators explain what the students are expected to demonstrate through completing the activities.

Teacher information has been provided to enhance the teacher's understanding of the concept being taught and to provide additional information to relate to the students. It also offers instructions for the activity.

Additional activities can be used to further develop the outcomes being assessed and clarify the concepts and skills taught in the activity. The additional activities may involve other curriculum areas.

Answers to all worksheet activities are given. Some answers may need a teacher check, while others will vary, depending on the students' personal experiences and opinions.

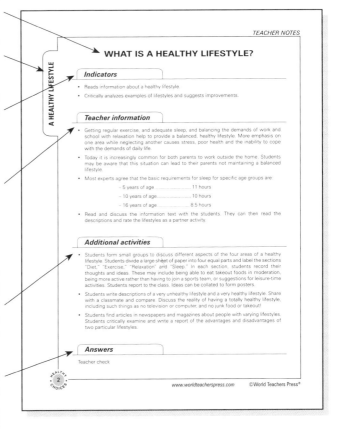

HEALTHY CHOICES

Student Worksheet

The student activities reinforce and develop understanding of the concept and are largely language-based. A variety of student worksheets is provided, which may contain information to read and discuss, as well as questions to answer.

The subtitle shows which of the four sections of the book is being covered.

The title shows the particular activity from the section being covered.

Most student pages begin with some **background information** which the student will need to complete the activities on the worksheet.

Questions to answer or activities to complete form the major part of the worksheet. All student instructions are concisely and clearly written to enable the students to work independently, if required.

The Health Challenge provides a practical application of the worksheet to be completed at home or independently by the student to link home and school.

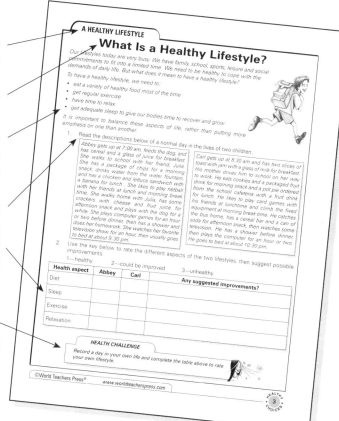

The final activity on each student worksheet—**Health Challenge**—is intended to extend learning about healthy lifestyles to the home environment. The emphasis in each Health Challenge is on the student to complete the activity, providing information to parents without being didactic or threatening in any way. These activities need not be corrected by the teacher, but may be used as a homework activity, if desired. It is hoped that through this activity, home and school may work together to develop a better awareness of health issues facing the adults of the future.

Healthy Choices aims to introduce and develop the knowledge, skills, attitudes and values that will enable students to lead healthy and fulfilling lives. Students will consider what it means to be healthy—physically, socially, mentally and emotionally—and will be given tools to help them become responsible for their own well-being.

Many of the activities in this book provide students with an opportunity to formulate their thoughts on a topic and express their opinions and feelings. Classroom discussions are invaluable resources for encouraging critical and reflective thinking.

NOTE: It is especially important for teachers, teaching assistants and other adults working with the students to be aware of sensitive factors such as poor home background, economic factors and individual weight problems, which could cause some students to feel uncomfortable when completing these worksheets.

TEACHER INFORMATION

Assessment Forms

The following explanation details how to use the **Assessment Form—Knowledge** on page vii.

Learning Area	• Complete the appropriate learning area; for example: A healthy lifestyle.
Task(s)	• Give a brief description of the activity and what was expected of the students.
Assessment	• Write the relevant indicator(s) and assess appropriately.
Teacher Comment	• Use this space to comment on aspects of an individual student's performance which cannot be indicated in the formal assessment, such as work habits or particular needs or abilities.

The following explanation details how to use the **Assessment Form—Skills and Attitudes** on page viii.

Assessment	• Assess the specific development of an individual student in these areas.
Teacher Comment	• Use this space to comment on an individual student's skills and attitudes.

Student Forms

Although there are different types of diaries for food, exercise and sleep included in this book, the following additional forms have also been included on pages xiv – xix.

ASSESSMENT FORM — KNOWLEDGE

Name

Date

Learning Area

Task(s)

The student was asked to:

Outcome(s)

Assessment

The student:	Demonstrated	Needs further opportunity

Teacher Comment

ASSESSMENT FORM
— SKILLS AND ATTITUDES

Name

Date

Assessment

The student:	Demonstrated	Needs further opportunity
• recognizes the importance to personal health of physical activities		
• recognizes the importance to personal health of a balanced diet		
• recognizes the importance to personal health of adequate relaxation and sleep		
• makes decisions for himself/herself		
• displays evidence of self-management skills		
• participates in and enjoys group activities		
• sets personal goals		
• achieves personal goals		
• communicates effectively		
• listens effectively		
• appreciates the similarities and differences between himself/herself and others		
• has a positive self-image		
• shows sensitivity towards others		
• recognizes the need for balance between diet, exercise, relaxation and sleep		

Teacher Comment

www.worldteacherspress.com   ©World Teachers Press®

HEALTHY CHOICES

Glossary of terms

A

additive:	a substance added to a product to improve its quality or to preserve it
aerobic activity:	exercise in which the heartbeat increases above its normal rate for an extended period of time
allergen:	a substance which might produce an allergic reaction
anaerobic activity:	exercise done in quick, short bursts
artery:	a blood vessel which carries blood from the heart to other parts of the body
asthma:	a disorder of the airways which makes breathing difficult

B

blood cholesterol:	a group of steroid alcohols derived from plants and animals found in the blood, usually indicated in a range from low to high and associated with the risk of heart disease
blood pressure:	the pressure of the blood against the inner walls of the blood vessels
blood sugar:	the quantity or percentage of glucose in the blood. Blood sugar concentration is a factor in diabetes.
body image:	the way a person perceives his/her body to be or appear
brain:	a greyish-and-whitish mass of nerve tissues which fill the skull of humans and other vertebrates; the center of sensation, body coordination, thought and emotion; a part of the nervous system

C

cancer	an abnormal growth or tumor which often reoccurs
calorie:	a unit of measurement for the quantity of heat output or energy from a food source
carbohydrates:	a group of foods or organic compounds which include simple sugars, such as glucose and lactose, as well as polymers, such as cellulose, starch and glycogen
carbon dioxide:	a colorless, odorless, incombustible gas (CO_2) present in the atmosphere and formed during the action of breathing
cardiovascular:	relating to the blood vessels and the heart
cholesterol:	a sterol (steroid alcohol derived from plants or animals) found in bile and gallstones, and in the brain and blood
circulation:	the recurring movement of the blood through the various vessels of the body
confidence:	self-reliance, belief or assurance, boldness; trust, belief in the trustworthiness or reliability of a person or thing

D

daily intake:	the amount of a substance, particularly food or drink, consumed each day
dehydration:	the state of being deprived of water; to lose water or moisture

Glossary of terms

D

depression:	to suffer a state of feeling low in spirits, dejected, despondent; characterized by feelings of inadequacy, lowered activity, sadness and pessimism
diabetes:	a disease in which the ability of the body to use sugar is impaired and sugar appears abnormally in the urine. Symptoms often include an excessive need to urinate, excessive thirst, tiredness, blurred vision, recurrent skin infections and weight loss. Diabetes may take two forms— type 1 (insulin dependent diabetes), which is usually found in people under 40, and type 2 (non-insulin dependent diabetes), which is usually found in adults over 50. Type 1 is the more severe form. There is no known cure for diabetes. Treatment includes diet control and exercise, and tablets or insulin injections.
diet:	the quantities and composition of food taken and its effect on health
digestion:	the process by which food is taken into the systems of the body

E

eating disorder:	a lack of order in eating habits; non-usual eating habits
endorphin:	a natural, pain-killing hormone
energy:	the habit, ability or capacity of a person to carry out physical activity; exerting power; activity

F

fat:	fleshy; obese; having a comparatively high oil content
fast food:	food for sale, such as chicken, fries and hamburgers, which can be made quickly
fiber:	undigested food materials which can aid the removal of wastes from the body and provide bulk to the contents of the large intestine
fitness:	the state of being fit
flexibility:	the ability to bend

G

genetics:	the science of heredity, concerning likenesses and differences of related organisms flowing from the interaction of their genes and the environment
genetically-modified:	having had the genetic origin changed
goal:	something which is desired or to be attained requiring effort: an aim to an end
gymnastics:	exercises requiring flexibility, strength and agility
gymnasium:	a building or room equipped with facilities for gymnastics and sports

H

healthy:	having and enjoying good health
heart:	the organ which pumps blood throughout the body

HEALTHY CHOICES

Glossary of terms

H

heart disease:	any condition which adversely affects the actions of the heart
hobbies:	a leisure-time activity or pursuit; an activity done for recreation
hormones:	any of a group of various substances which are formed in cells in one part of an organism and transported to another part of the organism where they have an effect. Hormones may be of animal or plant origin
hypertension:	elevated blood pressure

J

joints:	the movable places or parts where two bones or body segments join
junk food:	food which is thought to have little nutritional value, such as chips, etc.

K

kidneys:	a pair of bean-shaped glandular organs, situated at the back of the abdominal cavity, which excrete urine

L

legumes:	plants that bear their seeds in pods, such as peas and beans
leisure:	time free from the demands of work or duty
lethargy:	the state of being drowsy or lacking in energy; sluggish, apathetic
lethargic:	relating to lethargy; drowsy, sluggish
lifestyle:	the type of life chosen by an individual or group
ligament:	a band of tissue which serves to connect bones or hold organs in place
lungs:	two saclike respiratory organs in the thorax of humans and the higher vertebrates

M

minerals:	a substance occurring in nature with a definite chemical composition
muscles:	a group of fibers which enable movement

N

nerves:	one or more bundles of fibers forming part of the system which conveys impulses of sensation, motion, etc., between the brain or spinal cord and other parts of the body
nervous system:	the system of nerves and nerve centers in a human or animal
nutrient:	nourishing; providing goodness or nutriment
nutrition:	the act or process of nourishing or being nourished; food; nutriment
nutritional panel:	a table on the packaging of a food product which supplies details of what the food contains

Glossary of terms

O

obesity:	the state of being excessively fat
overweight:	extra or excess weight; weighing more than normal
oxygen:	a colorless, odorless gaseous element, constituting about one-fifth of the volume of the atmosphere and present in a combined state in nature; vital for aerobic respiration

P

passive smoking:	the inhaling by a non-smoker of the smoke produced by cigarette, cigar or pipe smokers
pedometer:	an instrument for recording the number of steps taken in walking, showing the total distance traveled
peer pressure:	pressure from friends or workmates to behave in a prescribed manner
personal skills:	those skills or abilities needed to deal well with other people
perspiration:	the act or process of perspiring; sweating; sweat
physical activity:	activity which requires the use of the body
pollution:	the act of making the environment dirty or unclean
preservatives:	a substance used to keep food fresh or extend its life
processed food:	food which has been changed or modified
protein:	a common name given to the food group which contains meat, fish, eggs, cheese, milk, yogurt, etc.

R

relaxation:	a state of relief of the body or mind from effort or application; a diversion or entertainment
respiration:	the act of respiring; inhaling and exhaling air; breathing

S

sedentary:	requiring a sitting posture; seldom moving about; lack of physical activity
self-esteem:	favorable opinion of oneself
skeleton:	the bones of a human or animal joined together to form a framework which supports the organs, muscles, tissues, etc.
skin cancer:	a tumor or melanoma occurring on the skin
social skills:	skills or attributes which enable a person to work or associate well with other people
sodium:	a soft, silver-white metallic element which oxidizes rapidly in moist air; sodium chloride is the chemical name for table salt
spinal cord:	the cord of nervous tissue extending through the spinal column

HEALTHY CHOICES

Glossary of terms

S

sport: an activity pursued for exercise or pleasure, usually requiring some form of physical expertise or competence

stress: to emphasize, to worry about, to attach importance or significance upon something

stroke: a sudden interruption of blood supply to the brain caused by a hemorrhage, thrombosis, or embolism

sugar: a sweet crystalline substance, derived mainly from the sugar cane or sugar beet plant, extensively used when cooking

system: a combination of body parts which, when joined, form a whole; for example, respiratory system, circulatory system

T

tendon: a band of tough, white tissue which connects a muscle with a bone

training: drill; education; to make fit by regular exercise and diet

V

vitamins: any of a group of food factors essential in small amounts to sustain life; the absence of any one of them results in a deficiency disease

volleyball: a game played in a gymnasium or outdoors with a large ball being struck by hand or arm from side to side, over a high net. The ball is not to hit the ground.

W

weight: how heavy something is; mass

wastes: products eliminated from the body and considered to be of no further use

Y

yoga: a series of movements or postures designed to develop flexibility and relaxation skills

HEALTHY EATING PLAN

Name

Date

Breakfast
Healthy snack
Lunch
Healthy snack
Dinner
Tally of the number of glasses of water drunk

HEALTHY CHOICES

BALANCED DIET PLAN

Name

Date

	bread, pasta, rice, cereal, noodles	vegetables	fruit	meat, poultry, fish, legumes, eggs, nuts	milk, yogurt, cheese	water
Breakfast						
Lunch						
Dinner			-			
Snacks						

www.worldteacherspress.com

HEALTHY · XV · CHOICES

HEALTHY RECIPE

Name

Date

Recipe name:

Equipment you will need:

Ingredients you will need:

What to do:

Make your recipe, with the help of an adult if necessary.

How does it taste?

Could you follow the steps easily?   YES   NO   SOMETIMES

EXERCISE DIARY

Name

Day	What did you do?	How long did you do it?	Who did it with you?
Monday _____ date			
Tuesday _____ date			
Wednesday _____ date			
Thursday _____ date			
Friday _____ date			
Saturday _____ date			
Sunday _____ date			
Incidental movement			

FOOD AND EXERCISE DIARY

Name

	Food				Exercise
	Breakfast	Lunch	Dinner	Snacks	Type/Time spent
Monday ———— date					
Tuesday ———— date					
Wednesday ———— date					
Thursday ———— date					
Friday ———— date					
Saturday ———— date					
Sunday ———— date					

www.worldteacherspress.com   ©World Teachers Press®

HEALTHY GOALS PLAN

Name

Date

Target date

This goal is important because ...

Steps to achieve my goal

Difficulties which may occur

Goal

I will know I have achieved my goal when ...

www.worldteacherspress.com

A HEALTHY LIFESTYLE

WHAT IS A HEALTHY LIFESTYLE?

Indicators

- Reads information about a healthy lifestyle.
- Critically analyzes examples of lifestyles and suggests improvements.

Teacher information

- Getting regular exercise and adequate sleep, and balancing the demands of work and school with relaxation help to provide a balanced, healthy lifestyle. More emphasis on one area while neglecting another causes stress, poor health and the inability to cope with the demands of daily life.

- Today it is increasingly common for both parents to work outside the home. Students may be aware that this situation can lead to their parents not maintaining a balanced lifestyle.

- Most experts agree that the basic requirements for sleep for specific age groups are:

  – 5 years of age .... 11 hours

  – 10 years of age .... 10 hours

  – 16 years of age .... 8.5 hours

- Read and discuss the information text with the students. They can then read the descriptions and rate the lifestyles as a partner activity.

Additional activities

- Students form small groups to discuss different aspects of the four areas of a healthy lifestyle. Students divide a large sheet of paper into four equal parts and label the sections "Diet," "Exercise," "Relaxation" and "Sleep." In each section, students record their thoughts and ideas. These may include being able to eat takeout foods in moderation, being more active rather than having to join a sports team, or suggestions for leisure-time activities. Students report to the class. Ideas can be collated to form posters.

- Students write descriptions of a very unhealthy lifestyle and a very healthy lifestyle. Share with a classmate and compare. Discuss the reality of having a totally healthy lifestyle, including such things as no television or computer, and no junk food or takeout!

- Students find articles in newspapers and magazines about people with varying lifestyles. Students critically examine and write a report of the advantages and disadvantages of two particular lifestyles.

Answers

Teacher check

What Is a Healthy Lifestyle?

Our lifestyles today are very busy. We have family, school, sports, leisure and social commitments to fit into a limited time. We need to be healthy to cope with the demands of daily life. But what does it mean to have a healthy lifestyle?

To have a healthy lifestyle, we need to:

- *eat a variety of healthy food most of the time*
- *get regular exercise*
- *have time to relax*
- *get adequate sleep to give our bodies time to recover and grow*

It is important to balance these aspects of life, rather than putting more emphasis on one than another.

1. Read the descriptions below of a normal day in the lives of two children.

Abbey gets up at 7:00 am, feeds the dog, and has cereal and a glass of juice for breakfast. She walks to school with her friend, Julia. She has a package of chips for a morning snack, drinks water from the water fountain, and has a chicken and lettuce sandwich with a banana for lunch. She likes to play soccer with her friends at lunch and morning break time. She walks home with Julia, has some crackers with cheese and fruit juice for afternoon snack and plays with the dog for a while. She plays computer games for an hour or two before dinner, then has a shower and does her homework. She watches her favorite television show for an hour, then usually goes to bed at about 9:30 pm.	*Carl gets up at 8:30 am and has two slices of toast with jam with a glass of milk for breakfast. His mother drives him to school on her way to work. He eats cookies and a packaged fruit drink for morning snack and a pot pie ordered from the school cafeteria with a fruit drink for lunch. He likes to play card games with his friends at lunchtime and climb the fixed equipment at morning break time. He catches the bus home, has a cereal bar and a can of soda for afternoon snack, then watches some television. He has a shower before dinner, then plays the computer for an hour or two. He goes to bed at about 10:30 pm.*

2. Use the key below to rate the different aspects of the two lifestyles, then suggest possible improvements.

1—healthy   2—could be improved   3—unhealthy

Health aspect	Abbey	Carl	Any suggested improvements?
Diet			
Sleep			
Exercise			
Relaxation			

HEALTH CHALLENGE

Record a day in your own life and complete the table above to rate your own lifestyle.

A HEALTHY LIFESTYLE

BENEFITS OF A HEALTHY LIFESTYLE

Indicator

- List five reasons for having a healthy lifestyle.

Teacher information

- There are great concerns about the increase in childhood obesity. One cause is sedentary time spent using the computer, PlayStations™ and Xboxes®, or watching television. Most families are very busy with many activities, so it is necessary to drive instead of walk from one place to another to fit everything in. There also seems to be an unlimited variety of food choices available, which often makes it more difficult to make healthy choices.

- The benefits of a healthy lifestyle include:
  - having more energy
  - looking good
  - feeling good
  - improved sleep and relaxation patterns
  - prevention of heart disease, cancer, type 2 diabetes
  - fighting illness
  - ability to concentrate better
  - improved fitness, including strength, endurance and flexibility
  - improved confidence

- Students will need to form groups of four or five to complete the worksheet. If some groups are having difficulty brainstorming benefits of a healthy lifestyle, suggest one of the benefits above to promote discussion.

Additional activities

- In groups, students select one of the benefits of a healthy lifestyle and list activities to achieve this benefit.
- Students write raps encouraging others to lead a healthy lifestyle.
- Students write an acrostic or crossword puzzle using words from the list of benefits.

Answers

1. Answers will vary but should include some of the benefits listed in the teacher information.
2–5. Teacher check

Benefits of a Healthy Lifestyle

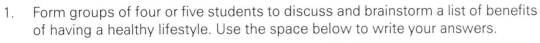

Balancing diet, exercise, sleep and relaxation will create a healthy lifestyle. There are many benefits of having a healthy lifestyle.

1. Form groups of four or five students to discuss and brainstorm a list of benefits of having a healthy lifestyle. Use the space below to write your answers.

   Benefits of a healthy lifestyle

2. As a group, number the benefits you have listed in order of importance from 1, 2, 3 and so on.

3. Complete the sentences.

   (a) Our group thought that the most important benefit of having a healthy lifestyle is

   _____

   (b) Our group thought that the least important benefit of having a healthy lifestyle is

   _____

4. Share your findings with the class and record any additional benefits mentioned in the box below.

5. Tally all the answers from the class and write the four most common answers.

   • _____

   • _____

   • _____

   • _____

HEALTH CHALLENGE

Select one of answers to Question 5 and find one way to achieve this benefit. For example, if the benefit is "to feel good" then try leading a healthy lifestyle for one week to see if you do feel better!

HOW HEALTHY IS YOUR LIFESTYLE?

A HEALTHY LIFESTYLE

Indicators

- Evaluates his/her own lifestyle.

- Suggests improvements to his/her own lifestyle where necessary.

Teacher information

- Students are constantly bombarded by health messages in the media, both good and bad. Most students have a basic understanding of what healthy foods to eat and of the need to exercise to stay healthy. They may not be aware of the need to get adequate relaxation or the number of hours of sleep required for growing bodies (10–16 years of age—between 10 hours and 8.5 hours of sleep each night). They may also not be aware of the exact number of hours spent doing sedentary activities, such as sitting at the computer. This is one aspect of their lifestyle which may need to be self-monitored. They should be made aware that it is okay to occasionally have fast foods and treats such as candy, ice cream, cookies and cake. The important thing is that they are leading a healthy lifestyle most of the time.

- Students read the information and complete the table in Question 1 independently. They can then evaluate their lifestyle based on the information in the table to complete Question 2.

- Students complete Question 3 by suggesting ways to improve two areas of their lifestyle.

Additional activities

- Students form small groups to share their evaluation worksheet and to discuss suggestions for changes to their lifestyles. Students who are shy or embarrassed about their lifestyle need not be forced to show their sheet to others.

- Students work with a partner to create an "ideal" lifestyle for a fictitious character.

- Students research to find magazine or newspaper articles where information is given about the lifestyles of favorite sports or media personalities. Students objectively evaluate their lifestyles.

Answers

Teacher check

How Healthy Is Your Lifestyle?

We can all lead a healthy lifestyle. All it takes is a little knowledge and lots of motivation!

There may be aspects of your lifestyle which are already reasonably healthy and may need only minor changes, while other areas may need lots of changes made.

1. Use the table below to find out how healthy your lifestyle is.

Diet

(a) I eat healthy food most of the time. ☐

(b) I eat fast food occasionally. ☐

(c) I eat fast food at least once a week. ☐

Exercise

(a) I get a lot of exercise. ☐

(b) I get some exercise occasionally. ☐

(c) I do not get very much exercise. ☐

Sleep

(a) I get at least nine hours of sleep each night. ☐

(b) I get between eight and nine hours of sleep each night. ☐

(c) I get less than eight hours of sleep each night. ☐

Relaxation

(a) I manage to relax each day. ☐

(b) I try to relax each day. ☐

(c) I don't relax very much at all. ☐

2. Evaluate your lifestyle.

   (a) If you checked mostly in the "a" boxes:

   > Great! Your lifestyle is very healthy.

   (b) If you checked mostly in the "b" boxes:

   > You're okay but there is room for improvement!

   (c) If you checked mostly in the "c" boxes:

   > Oh dear! Some lifestyle changes are needed.

3. Select two of the areas above—diet, sleep, relaxation, or exercise—where you could make some lifestyle changes and list some suggestions for carrying out these changes. For example, if you checked (c) for diet, you may suggest reducing the number of times that fast food is eaten or trying a healthier, homemade version of a fast food.

_____

_____

_____

_____

HEALTH CHALLENGE

Select one of your suggestions in Question 3 and try to carry it out over a period of two weeks or a month.

WHAT FACTORS AFFECT A HEALTHY LIFESTYLE? – 1

Indicator

- Reads information about factors which affect a healthy lifestyle.

Teacher information

- Students can discuss and record factors affecting a healthy lifestyle as a class before reading the text on page 9.

- Students read the information and use this to answer the questions on page 11. Discuss any unfamiliar vocabulary with the students after they have highlighted keywords and phrases.

Additional activities

- Students create a collage of factors which influence a healthy lifestyle, using one pictorial representation of each factor and a bold heading.

- Students write and role-play various situations which show a factor influencing lifestyle.

- Students write a poem or story about the life of a child affected by an unhealthy environment.

What Factors Affect a Healthy Lifestyle? – 1

Read the information below, highlighting any keywords or phrases in each paragraph.

There are many factors which may have an influence on adults and children being able to lead a healthy lifestyle.

People's lives today are very busy. Often, both parents work outside the home. Children are expected to take on more responsibility at home to help their parents. They also have sports and leisure commitments, as well as school responsibilities. They need time to socialize with their friends and be involved in family activities.

This "busy"ness also adds another factor: the need to use cars to get from one place to another quickly.

Today, society places a lot of emphasis on technology. Computers, DVDs, CDs, television, videos, PlayStations™ and Xboxes® have become major leisure activities, rather than traditional more active pursuits. This has led to a more sedentary lifestyle.

The media provides entertainment and information. Unfortunately, it also promotes fast food which fits easily into busy lifestyles. It is much more convenient at times to "grab" a quick takeout meal rather than prepare a meal. The media constantly bombards their audience with "perfect" body images, the need to buy the most fashionable clothes, the most up-to-date computer games, the best places to go, and the best things to do.

Cultural background may influence lifestyle. Girls from a number of different cultures may be discouraged from participating in active pursuits. Religious beliefs may prohibit children from participating in some activities which could encourage a healthier lifestyle.

Environments vary. We may be exposed to pollution, such as cigarette smoke. This can be detrimental to people who suffer from allergies, asthma, or other breathing difficulties. Environments where passive smoking is unavoidable make it difficult to lead a healthy lifestyle.

It is important for everyone to be accepted and cared about by family and friends. Both of these groups can influence people—positively or negatively. Negative feelings can lead people to adopt an unhealthy lifestyle.

A number of other factors also have an influence. These include economic factors within families which may prevent them from being able to afford to participate in certain healthy activities. There may also be a lack of affordable facilities to allow people to participate in active pursuits.

Perhaps the most important factor influencing healthy lifestyles is motivation, or the desire to be healthy. Any person who wants to be healthy will find a way to be healthy—if he/she is motivated enough!

HEALTH CHALLENGE

Think about your lifestyle and the factors that make it the way it is. What factors are within your power to change?

WHAT FACTORS AFFECT A HEALTHY LIFESTYLE? – 2

Indicator

• Completes questions about factors which influence the ability to have a healthy lifestyle.

Teacher information

• Students will need to use the information on page 9 to complete this worksheet.

• Note: Issues regarding cultural influences should be discussed with sensitivity. Students with different cultural backgrounds or religious beliefs should not feel they must justify their culture. However, talking about these factors with the remainder of the class may result in a greater understanding of different cultures.

• Other factors to answer Question 3 may be added from previous discussions.

Additional activities

• Students discuss and compare answers to Questions 2 and 3.

• Students list suggestions for making the best use of a busy lifestyle.

• Students compile questions for grandparents about their lifestyles, then interview them to compare with their own lifestyle.

Answers

1. Answers should include eight of the following: motivation, busy lifestyles, dependence upon cars, sedentary lifestyles, media, culture, environments, influence of family or friends, economic factors, availability of facilities

2. Teacher check

3. Teacher check

What Factors Affect a Healthy Lifestyle? – 2

Complete the questions, using the information which you highlighted on page 9.

1. List eight factors which may influence a person's ability to have a healthy lifestyle.

    *   _____
    *   _____
    *   _____
    *   _____
    *   _____
    *   _____
    *   _____
    *   _____

2. In each box below, give an example of how these factors may influence the ability to have a healthy lifestyle. For example, under the heading of "Busy lives," you "may" write "no time to fit in exercise" or "junk food eaten too often."

Busy lives	Cars	Technology	Media
Culture	Environment	Family/Friends	Motivation

3. List any other factors which you feel may influence the ability to have a healthy lifestyle.

HEALTH CHALLENGE

Think about the influence other people have on you. Is it a good or bad influence? Become more aware of why you do something!

A HEALTHY LIFESTYLE

WHAT FACTORS AFFECT YOUR LIFESTYLE?

Indicator

• Completes information about factors which affect his/her ability to have a healthy lifestyle.

Teacher information

• Students should have read the information text on page 9 before completing this worksheet.

• Students complete the worksheet independently, then compare his/her answers with three other class members to find common factors.

• Should there be few common factors, students should be allowed to simply share their answers.

Additional activities

• Students choose one of the factors affecting lifestyle and create posters motivating other students to try to alleviate the influence. For example, to encourage students to use cars less where possible, they may write catchy sayings such as "Walk, don't ride! It's good for your heart and good for the environment!"

• Students write raps to popular music which motivate students to improve their lifestyles.

• Students write healthy food advertisements to encourage students to eat better.

Answers

Teacher check

What Factors Affect Your Lifestyle?

1. Using the information on page 9 and your own knowledge, complete the table below about factors affecting your lifestyle.

Factor affecting lifestyle	Way each factor affects lifestyle

2. Form small groups of four students and compare your table. List any factors affecting lifestyle which are common to all members of the group.

_____

_____

_____

_____

_____

_____

_____

HEALTH CHALLENGE

Select one of the common factors above and find a way to change it if possible.

BRANDEN'S DIARY

Indicator

- Reads a diary entry which gives information about factors which influence a healthy lifestyle.

Teacher information

- Boredom can be one reason why children and adults eat unnecessarily, adding extra calories to an average dietary intake. Eating when doing other activities can often be a problem as well. Children (or adults) should not eat, if possible, while watching television or using the computer because they may not be aware of the amount consumed.

- Other factors include trying to lose weight by, using fad diets or "quick fixes" rather than eating healthy food and exercising more.

- Environments can be unhealthy for a number of reasons. Reasons include lack of proper hygiene, which encourages disease, and cigarette smoke, which provides opportunities for passive smoking.

- Role models play an important part in relaying correct health messages. Parents who engage in an unhealthy lifestyle send the same message to their children. Teachers can try to act as role models where possible. Often children may provide a good motivation to encourage a parent to make a lifestyle change.

- Students read the diary entry, then answer the questions independently. Discuss answers as a class.

Additional activities

- Students write a diary entry of their own about a normal day in their life, relating it to health issues such as diet and exercise.

- Students research to investigate various fad diets and dissect these using their background knowledge of what a healthy diet entails.

- Students make a list of quick, fun activities to do when boredom sets in.

Answers

Teacher check

Branden's Diary

1. Read the diary entry below, which tells of a day in the life of a 12-year-old boy.

Dear Diary,

Mom was still at work when I got home and I had to stay inside after I did my chores because she said so! It's not as though I'm a little kid! I can look after myself—well, most of the time anyway!

Danny was sick at school today. He has diabetes and, he had to have his insulin shot. He really looked awful! But he always seems happy, and his diabetes never seems to stop him from doing stuff that the other guys do!

It got me thinking about how unhealthy I am. I mean, I know I'm not going to die tomorrow or anything, but I get worried sometimes! Take for instance this afternoon. When I got home, I had my usual bowl of cereal and two small packages of chips and a can of soda. I felt a bit sick afterwards, but I was bored and there was nothing else to do except watch television!

Maybe I need to go on a diet or something. I could try cutting out some meals or snacks for a while. Maybe I would lose some weight that way. Nigel at school is really popular with the other kids, and he is really skinny!

I worry about Mom a lot. She works really long hours to buy me stuff like the other kids, but I would rather have her at home more. She worries a lot about paying all the bills. When she gets stressed out, she smokes more. I wonder if I will be a smoker when I get older. It looks and smells bad, but it can't be that bad, even with all those anti-smoking ads on TV; otherwise, Mom probably wouldn't do it! Still, I'm glad I don't smoke!

Yikes! Gotta go! I forgot to bring in the laundry for Mom and I can hear her car coming up the driveway!

Branden

2. Write two reasons why Branden's lifestyle is unhealthy and explain why.

    *   _____
        _____
    *   _____
        _____

3. Select an unhealthy lifestyle choice Branden is considering. Explain why it is unhealthy.

    _____

HEALTH CHALLENGE

Avoid situations where there may be cigarette smoke.
Passive smoking is hazardous to your health!

A HEALTHY LIFESTYLE

THE EFFECTS OF AN UNHEALTHY LIFESTYLE – 1

Indicator

- Reads information about the effects of an unhealthy lifestyle.

Teacher information

- Students read the information and highlight any important keywords and phrases.

- Students will need a dictionary to find the meanings of any unknown words.

- The information text can be discussed and other information supplied by the students where applicable.

Additional activities

- Invite a parent or teacher who has type 2 diabetes or a heart problem to speak to the class. Encourage the students to ask questions about how they cope with their health problem using diet, exercise and medication.

- Students design a basic exercise program for seniors which aims to strengthen bones.

- Visit a gym and have a fitness instructor explain to the students what the various apparatus are for and how they help different parts of the body. If possible, allow the students to use the equipment.

- Students design his/her own fitness circuit using equipment available at school. Ensure that students properly understand the appropriate exercises which can be done on each piece of equipment and which parts of the body the exercises benefit.

Answers

Teacher check

The Effects of an Unhealthy Lifestyle – 1

1. Read the text below and highlight any keywords or phrases.

Did you know that a gym recently opened in Britain—just for kids? Not a good idea you think! No one will go! Wrong! Five hundred children enrolled in the first week!

Today, obesity in children is increasing at an alarming rate. Children are unhealthier today than they have ever been.

Worldwide, less healthy diets and less active lifestyles have caused childhood obesity levels to climb dramatically.

An unhealthy lifestyle can cause many problems now as well as later in life.

Health experts' main concern is that overweight children will develop health problems such as heart disease, cancer and type 2 diabetes later in life. Excess fatty deposits can prevent the heart from pumping blood effectively around the body, leading to high blood pressure and the possibility of stroke and heart attack.

More and more children are being diagnosed with type 2 diabetes, which affects the body's ability to use sugar effectively and can lead to kidney disease, blindness and foot or leg amputation. There is no cure for type 2 diabetes, but it may be improved or controlled by a healthy diet and adequate exercise.

The ability of the body to fight various types of disease is decreased if it is not in good condition.

When the correct fuel is put into a car, it runs well. If the wrong fuel is used, it may cough and sputter and not work properly. The same applies to our bodies. If we feed them the correct fuel and keep them tuned with exercise, they will work well and do what we want them to do. We will have the energy to do the things that we need to do.

Being overweight puts extra pressure on joints such as the knees, because of the extra weight they have to carry. This can make it difficult to move around, which in turn makes it more difficult to exercise and further adds to the problem.

People with an existing health problem need to stay fit and well in order to not aggravate the condition. Often, having this type of problem can force people to be more active. There are many well-known swimmers who began to exercise in the pool to build up their lung capacity to alleviate health problems such as asthma.

Weight-bearing exercise, such as lifting light weights, is known to have a positive effect in strengthening bones. Even senior citizens have found that after commencing weight-bearing exercise, the strength of their bones has increased and their bones are less likely to break as a result of osteoporosis.

2. Underline any unknown words and find the meanings of these in the dictionary before answering the questions on page 19.

HEALTH CHALLENGE

Interview a neighbor, family friend, or relative about a negative or positive change in his/her lifestyle and how he/she feels.

HEALTHY CHOICES

17

A HEALTHY LIFESTYLE

THE EFFECTS OF AN UNHEALTHY LIFESTYLE – 2

Indicator

- Completes questions about the effects of an unhealthy lifestyle.

Teacher information

- Students will need to have read the information on page 17 before completing the questions on this worksheet.

- Students complete the answers to Questions 1 to 6 independently. Question 6 may be discussed as a class once students have completed their answers.

Additional activities

- Students survey class members to see how many students exercise regularly and the types of exercise done. Students create a graph using the results of the survey.

- Students can use the results of the survey to tally the types of exercise done and show the various parts of the body being exercised. Students create a report to show those areas of the body which are exercised the least.

- Students invite a group of seniors to demonstrate the types of exercise done in an exercise class. Alternatively, students may view a group of seniors exercising in a seniors gym class.

Answers

1. Health experts are concerned that overweight children will develop health problems later in life.

2. The three major problems are heart disease, cancer and type 2 diabetes.

3. It is important to keep the body in good condition so that it is able to fight various diseases.

4. (a) "... the energy to do the things we want to do."

   (b) "... put extra pressure on joints such as the knees as they have extra weight to carry."

   (c) "... need to stay fit and well in order to not make their existing health problem worse."

5. (a) true (b) false (c) false (d) true (e) false (f) false

6. Teacher check

The Effects of an Unhealthy Lifestyle – 2

Use the information on page 17 to answer the questions.

1. Why are health experts so concerned about the health of children today?

   _____

   _____

   _____

Health hazard ahead!

2. What are the three major health problems facing overweight children later in life?

①	②	③

3. Give one reason why is it important to keep your body in good condition.

   _____

4. Complete these sentences from the text.

   (a) "If we feed our bodies the correct fuel and keep them tuned with exercise, they will

   work well and we will have _____

   _____."

   (b) Being overweight can _____

   _____.

   (c) People with existing health problems _____

   _____

   _____.

5. Answer true or false.

   (a) Weight-bearing exercises can strengthen bones. | TRUE | FALSE |

   (b) Senior citizens cannot exercise. | TRUE | FALSE |

   (c) Changes in lifestyles have not affected children's health. | TRUE | FALSE |

   (d) An unhealthy diet and lack of exercise has caused obesity levels to rise. | TRUE | FALSE |

   (e) Fatty deposits around the heart are not harmful. | TRUE | FALSE |

   (f) People who have a health problem shouldn't do vigorous exercise. | TRUE | FALSE |

6. Do you think a children's gym is needed where you live? Explain why you think it would or would not work.

HEALTH CHALLENGE

Put only healthy "fuel" into your body for one week to see how your body feels.

CHLOE'S HEALTHY LIFESTYLE

Indicator

- Formulates an action plan to improve the lifestyle of a fictitious character.

Teacher information

- The aim of this activity is for the students to use the knowledge they have gained about what a healthy lifestyle means to formulate an action plan.

- Students read the description of Chloe's lifestyle and follow the format given to formulate an action plan to improve her lifestyle.

- Students should check the relevant boxes to select which areas need changing for (a).

- To complete section (b), if a student has checked the diet box in section (a) they may suggest that she eats pizza too often and not enough vegetables, etc.

- To complete section (c), students may offer specific suggestions such as eating some vegetables with lunch and the main meal of the day or only have pizza once every two weeks.

- Section (d) should indicate the ultimate goal for Chloe, such as being more active and eating more healthy food or even losing a little weight to improve her long-term health prospects.

Note: Students need to be aware that no one's lifestyle can be perfect and the occasional treat should be allowed.

Additional activities

- Students formulate an action plan to implement an "ideal" healthy lifestyle.

- Students create their own character with lifestyle imperfections for which a class member can formulate a relevant action plan.

- Students design a flow chart to show how improvements in lifestyle can have long-term benefits.

Answers

Teacher check

Chloe's Healthy Lifestyle

Chloe is a 12-year-old girl who is slightly overweight. Her dad, Bob, has just come home from the hospital after suffering chest pains. Bob has been told by his doctor that he needs to change his lifestyle dramatically; otherwise, he runs the risk of having a serious heart attack.

Chloe is a talented computer user who loves watching sports. She enjoys eating pizza and sleeping in on the weekends. Pasta and fruit are her favorite foods. Her favorite drinks are soft drinks, although her Mom doesn't let her have them very often. Chloe used to like going for bike rides with her Dad before her dad got sick. She also loves her golden retriever, Maxie. She has one younger brother, Harrison, who is really annoying at times, especially when he wants Chloe to show him how to do things on the computer.

1. Use the format below to create an action plan for Chloe to improve her lifestyle so that she does not have the same health problems as her dad later in life.

My action plan

(a) Chloe needs to improve these areas of her lifestyle:

☐ diet   ☐ exercise   ☐ sleep   ☐ relaxation

(b) She needs to improve these aspects of the areas listed above:

(c) She can improve these aspects by:

(d) If Chloe carries out these changes, she should find that ...

_____

_____

_____

HEALTH CHALLENGE

Create an action plan to make improvements in your own lifestyle. Don't forget that you are allowed treats occasionally!

WHAT IS A HEALTHY DIET?

A HEALTHY DIET

Indicators

- Reads information about a healthy diet.
- Answers questions about a healthy diet.

Teacher information

- The *Healthy Eating Guide* (see diagram on page 23) shows the foods needed for a healthy diet. The foods in the largest segment should provide the main part of our diet; the requirements get smaller as shown. Food servings eaten from each part of the guide each day should provide people with enough nutrients and energy to help them grow and keep healthy.

- The main food groups include:

  – *bread, cereals, rice, noodles, pasta.* This group provides carbohydrates, protein, fiber, some fat, iron and thiamin, magnesium, zinc, riboflavin, niacin equivalents, folate and sodium. Wholemeal and multigrain varieties contain more nutrients than white products, which are more highly processed.

  – *vegetables and legumes.* This group supplies vitamin A (beta-carotene), carbohydrates, fiber, magnesium, iron, vitamin C, folate and potassium.

  – *fruit.* This group provides vitamins (especially vitamin C), carbohydrates, fiber and folate. Fruit is sweet because of the natural sugar it contains. Dried fruit also belongs in this group, but it contains concentrated forms of sugar and should be eaten in smaller quantities.

  – *milk, yogurt, cheese.* This group provides calcium, protein, energy, fat, cholesterol, carbohydrates, magnesium, zinc, riboflavin, vitamin B12, sodium and potassium. There are many varieties in this group, including fresh, dried, evaporated and longlife products. The most important factor concerning this group is that it is the best source of calcium for healthy bones and teeth.

  – *meat, fish, poultry, eggs, nuts, legumes.* This group provides protein, iron, zinc, fat, cholesterol, niacin equivalents and vitamin B12. Iron supplements may be needed for vegetarians and those people who do not eat red meat.

  – *fats, oils and sugars* are not separately essential to our diet and should only be eaten in small amounts. Fats may be unsaturated, such as those in oils and margarines. Some may be beneficial in lowering cholesterol levels in the blood. Saturated fats can increase the risk of heart disease. They can be found in butter, lard and drippings. Sugar has little nutritional value, so foods with a high sugar content such as soft drinks, candy, jams, honey, cakes and cookies should be eaten in small quantities and considered "occasional treats."

- Individual and family eating patterns are greatly influenced by personal, social and cultural practices. Other factors which influence a healthy diet include time constraints and the skills needed to prepare and cook food.

- Have the students read the information text, then study the *Healthy Eating Guide* as a class. Discuss the different amounts of different types of food that should be eaten. The students can then complete the questions. They will require an encyclopedia for Question 1. This question could be completed in pairs.

Additional activities

- In small groups, create posters featuring a type of healthy food and its benefits to our health.
- Conduct a survey among the students at the school to find out their favorite healthy foods. Create a healthy school cafeteria/snack bar menu based on the answers.

Answers

1. Answers will vary, but may include the following:

   (a) provide energy for the body

   (b) assists the function of the stomach and intestines

   (c) helps to strengthen bones and teeth, helps blood to clot and muscles to contract

   (d) provides energy for the body and helps to repair and build tissue

   (e) helps with the normal functioning of cells and tissues

   (f) helps with growth and healing

2. Teacher check

What Is a Healthy Diet?

Have you ever heard the saying "You are what you eat"? It's true! Sticking to a healthy diet means you will look and feel your best. But how do we know exactly what a healthy diet is? Using the Healthy Eating Guide *is a good way to help us understand this. It shows the proportion of different types of foods we should eat each day.*

- *The types of foods you should eat the most are bread, cereal, rice, pasta and noodles. These foods are excellent sources of carbohydrates.*

- *Vegetables, legumes and fruit are given an important emphasis on the diagram because they are loaded with vitamins, minerals, carbohydrates and fiber.*

- *Milk, yogurt and cheese are important because they are an excellent source of calcium and protein.*

- *Lean meat, fish, poultry, eggs, nuts and legumes provide us with protein, iron and zinc.*

- *Fats, oils and sugars are not listed in the diagram as, separately, they are not essential to our diet and should only be eaten in small amounts.*

Answer these questions.

1. Use an encyclopedia to write one way each of these assists our bodies.

   (a) carbohydrates _____

   (b) fiber _____

   (c) calcium _____

   (d) protein _____

   (e) iron _____

   (f) zinc _____

2. Using the *Healthy Eating Guide*, plan a day's meals and snacks that you would enjoy.

Breakfast	Snack	Lunch	Snack	Dinner

HEALTH CHALLENGE

Each day for one week, try eating a healthy food you have never tried.

HEALTHY DIET GUIDE DESIGN

Indicator

- Designs a healthy diet guide based on the *Healthy Eating Guide*.

Teacher information

- Students should be familiar with the *Healthy Eating Guide* diagram on page 23.

- Read and discuss the information in Question 1 with the students to ensure they understand each of the areas they must consider for their designs. Ask for volunteers to provide some ideas. The students can then complete Question 2 individually.

- Provide the students with large sheets of paper or posterboard to create the final copy of their designs. The posters could then be displayed in the classroom or given to classes of younger students to display in their classrooms.

Additional activities

- Invite a worker involved in nutritional health to speak to the class about tips on making their diets healthier.

- Students write everything they eat during one day. They can then use the *Healthy Eating Guide* to find out how healthy their daily diet is and where they need to improve.

Answers

Answers will vary

Healthy Diet Guide Design

The Healthy Eating Guide *was designed to make it easy for people to understand what they should eat.*

Imagine you work for a health organization. You decide to create a colorful and creative new way to show the same information that you can put on posters, stickers and magnets.

1. Plan your design by following the steps below.

   • **Shape(s)**

   Instead of a circle, what other shape(s) could you use to show the different amounts of food people should eat? How could you arrange your design on a poster?

   _____

   _____

   _____

   • **Pictures/Icons**

   How will you represent the different food groups? The image should be eye-catching. You might consider making the healthier foods look more attractive than the fats and oils!

   _____

   _____

   _____

   • **Colors**

   What colors will grab people's attention? What color could you use for the different food groups?

   _____

   _____

   _____

2. Sketch your ideas in the box.

3. Create your design on a large sheet of posterboard or paper. Add a name for your design; e.g. "The Healthy Diet Triangle."

HEALTH CHALLENGE

Try healthier alternatives to your favorite junk foods; e.g., rice crackers instead of potato chips for a week.

BENEFITS OF A HEALTHY DIET

A HEALTHY DIET

Indicators

• Reads information about the benefits of a healthy diet.

• Answers questions about the benefits of a healthy diet.

Teacher information

• Individual and family patterns of eating are greatly influenced by personal, social and cultural reasons. Other factors which influence the availability of a healthy diet include time constraints and the skills needed to prepare and cook food.

• Childhood obesity is becoming one of the biggest health threats of the century. It is increasing at an alarming rate due to increased food intake and physical inactivity. It is essential to try to prevent obesity in children, as this can lead to illness and cancer later in life. Increasing numbers of children and adults are developing type 2 diabetes and heart problems. Obese children and adolescents have low self-esteem and body dissatisfaction. They are less likely to do well academically, have poor job prospects, and are often socially isolated.

• Read the information text with the students. They can then complete the questions independently. The answers to Question 3 could be discussed as a class.

Note: The risk of developing type 2 diabetes can be lessened by maintaining a healthy lifestyle. Type 1 diabetes is hereditary and cannot be prevented.

Additional activities

• Write a list of foods that are high in saturated fat.

• Create an easy, healthy breakfast menu that students would enjoy.

• Survey the class to find out some of their favorite junk foods and why they enjoy them. Create a list of tasty, healthy alternatives to the favorite junk foods.

Answers

1. Because they are still growing and developing.

2. (a) Answers will vary, but should include three of the following: helps to prevent a range of diseases; provides fuel for growth and development; helps you to be a high achiever at school; makes you feel good about yourself.

   (b) Answers will vary, but should include three of the following: can cause health problems like heart disease, type 2 diabetes, some cancers, high blood pressure, becoming overweight, high blood cholesterol, tooth decay and childhood obesity.

3. Teacher check

Benefits of a Healthy Diet

It is okay to eat unhealthy food occasionally. But people who eat junk food more than they should are at risk of developing some major health problems, including heart disease, type 2 diabetes, some cancers and high blood pressure. Becoming overweight is a common effect of eating unhealthy food. This is because many junk foods are loaded with fat, which is very high in calories. The worst type of fat is "saturated" fat (the main fat in animal products), which increases blood cholesterol levels. Foods high in sugar are not much better. You probably already know that eating foods high in sugar causes tooth decay. There is also evidence to suggest that eating lots of sugar contributes to childhood obesity.

As well as avoiding unhealthy food, we should eat a wide range of healthy food. This is because different foods contain different compounds that help to prevent a range of diseases, which is especially the case with "plant" foods like fruit, vegetables and grains.

Having a healthy diet is important for everyone, but it is vital for children because they are still growing and developing. This takes up a lot of energy, requiring good quality food "fuel." Studies have also found that children who eat a healthy breakfast are higher achievers at school. As an added bonus, you will find that having a healthy diet generally makes you feel good about yourself.

So, are you eating healthy food?

Answer these questions.

1. Why is it especially important for children to follow a healthy diet?

2. (a) List three benefits of following a healthy diet.

   _____

   _____

   (b) List three problems that eating too much junk food can cause.

   _____

   _____

3. Give some reasons why you think some people might eat too much junk food.

HEALTH CHALLENGE

Substitute water or plain milk for soft drinks whenever you can. Soft drinks are loaded with sugar.

FRUITS AND VEGETABLES

Indicator

- Researches nutritional information about a fruit or vegetable.

Teacher information

- Properly defined, a fruit is the part of a flowering plant that holds its seeds. This means that foods we may consider to be vegetables (like tomatoes) are actually fruits. Most fruits are high in sugar and vitamins, but contain low levels of protein.

- Vegetables can come from a variety of plant parts—including the leaves, roots, seeds and stems. Most vegetables are a low-calorie source of vitamins and minerals, including vitamins A and C, calcium and iron.

- The students will need access to the Internet or other resources (like encyclopedias) to complete the questions. This could be done in pairs. When the questions have been completed, the answers should be shared with the class. A class "super-fruit" or "super-veggie" could be nominated!

Additional activities

- In small groups, create a television commercial that encourages people to eat fruits and vegetables.

- Plan and hold a class party that features fruit and vegetable recipes made by the students.

Answers

Answers will vary

Fruits and Vegetables

Use the Internet or other resources to investigate the qualities of a fruit or vegetable. If you are using the Internet, you can type this question into a search engine: "Why is/are (name of fruit or vegetable) good for us?" Use your research to complete the information below.

1. Check or write in the name of the fruit or vegetable you choose to research.

   fruits: ☐ bananas ☐ apples ☐ oranges other _____

   vegetables: ☐ spinach ☐ peppers ☐ eggplants other _____

2. Write a list of the nutrients this fruit or vegetable contains; e.g., types of vitamins or minerals, fiber.

3. Circle one of these nutrients. Explain some of the health benefits it gives us.

   _____

   _____

   _____

4. Write two interesting healthy facts about your fruit or vegetable.

   • _____

   • _____

5. Describe a simple, healthy recipe for young children that features your fruit or vegetable.

   Name of recipe:

   Ingredients:

   Method:

HEALTH CHALLENGE

If you don't enjoy eating vegetables very much, find some healthy recipes that make them more tasty. There are loads of these on the Internet!

DIET ISSUES

Indicators

- Reads information about fad diets and eating disorders.

- Answers questions about fad diets and eating disorders.

Teacher information

- Fad diets have become popular ways to lose weight quickly. There is a huge range of these to choose from. But these diets can be dangerous due to their lack of nutrients and their inability to provide adequate calories for energy use. Many people also find that they are unsuccessful at keeping off the weight they lost during the diet once they return to their normal eating habits. People who wish to lose weight should avoid fad diets and instead talk to a doctor or dietitian to follow a safe and healthy eating and exercise program.

- An eating disorder is a condition where a person has problems with his/her eating habits and body image. The majority of people with eating disorders are adolescent girls. Two of the most well-known eating disorders are anorexia nervosa and bulimia nervosa.

  A person with anorexia has an aversion to eating. They eat only tiny amounts of food and often overexercise. Although sufferers will become dangerously thin, losing more than 25 percent of their body weight, they believe they are overweight. This condition causes a range of health problems, such as low blood pressure and a slow heartbeat. Menstruation may also stop in girls. In addition, people with anorexia often isolate themselves socially.

  People with bulimia spend hours overeating, and then secretly get rid of the food by forcing themselves to vomit or by taking laxatives. It is sometimes difficult to spot someone who has bulimia because they have a more normal weight than people with anorexia. This condition also causes a range of health problems, such as damage to teeth and gums (from the acid in vomit) and dehydration. Like people suffering from anorexia, bulimics often isolate themselves socially.

  There are many causes for eating disorders, including low self-esteem, depression, stress and pressure by peers, or other influences to be thin.

- Read and discuss the information text with the students. Teachers may like to have extra information about eating disorders on hand to answer any of the students' questions. The topic should be treated with sensitivity and openness.

- The questions can be completed independently. The answers to Question 3 could be discussed with the class and could be used as a topic for debate.

Additional activities

- Invite a guest speaker who has recovered from an eating disorder to talk about his/her former condition and how he/she recovered.

- Discuss reasons why people want to be thin, including pressure from the media and friends.

Answers

1. (a) true (b) false (c) false

2. eat only one or a few types of food; boring; most people put on weight after they have finished the diet

3. Teacher check

Diet Issues

Magazines, television commercials and celebrities often lead us to believe that being thin is being "perfect." But what is a perfect body? In reality, it is different for everyone, depending on a person's height and build. Having a so-called perfect body is not important—following a healthy diet and exercising regularly is!

Unfortunately, many people don't see things this way and decide to go on "fad" diets to get thin quickly. This is different from trying to improve your diet by cutting out junk food or following a diet recommended by a doctor. Most fad diets are dangerous to your health. Often, they allow you to eat just one or a few types of food. This is not only extremely boring, it can mean you are receiving too few nutrients, or inadequate calories for energy use. And when most people finish these fad diets, guess what happens? They end up regaining any weight they have lost!

But some people are even more desperate to be thin and can develop a condition called an "eating disorder." One type of eating disorder is "anorexia nervosa." It mostly affects girls, but boys can develop it too. People with this disorder hardly eat anything and often overexercise. They become dangerously thin and may become so sick they end up in the hospital. Some of the problems anorexia can cause are low blood pressure, difficulty concentrating, and heart and liver damage.

Answer these questions.

1. True or false?

    (a) People go on "fad" diets to try to get thin quickly.

TRUE	FALSE

    (b) Anorexia is caused by low blood pressure.

TRUE	FALSE

    (c) Trying to be thin is more important than a healthy diet.

TRUE	FALSE

2. Write keywords or phrases used in the text to describe the problems with fad diets.

    lack of nutrients or inadequate calories for energy use

    Fad diets

3. Do you think thin bodies are perfect? Give reasons for your opinion.

    _____

    _____

    _____

HEALTH CHALLENGE

Think of some simple ways you could make your breakfast cover a variety of food groups; for example, putting fruit on your cereal, eating a microwave omelette with toast.

FAD DIET INTERVIEW

Indicators

- Researches and records information about fad diets.
- Plans and presents a television interview with a partner.

Teacher information

- Read the entire worksheet with the students, then ask them to find a partner to work with. The pairs will need access to the Internet or other resources containing information about fad diets to complete Question 1. Students may need to refer to the information from page 31 on "Diet Issues."

- For Questions 2 and 3, encourage the students to use the style of television current affairs programs with which they are familiar. Teachers may like to check the students' answers to Question 3 before they begin rehearsing their interviews.

- The interviews could be recorded with a video camera or presented live to the class. The students could also organize costumes and music to enhance their performances.

Additional activities

- Compare different fad diets to find out which are the most dangerous to a person's health.

Answers

Answers will vary

Fad Diet Interview

Find a partner with whom to plan and perform a television interview. One of you will be the interviewer and the other will be a nutritional expert. The interviewer is talking to the expert about the latest fad diet.

1. Begin by finding out some information about a fad diet. You might find this in magazines or on the Internet. Write some notes about the basic "rules" of the diet.

   Name of diet: _____

   Description:

2. Write some brief opening comments the interviewer can say to the television viewers about the dangers of fad diets. You can use the information from page 31 on "Diet issues." The interviewer can then introduce the expert.

   _____

   _____

   _____

   _____

   _____

3. The expert will need to answer six to eight questions about the diet during the interview. These questions should include a description of the diet and its dangers. You can also name some imaginary celebrities who are on the diet if you like! Decide on the questions with your partner and write them below.

   • _____

   • _____

   • _____

   • _____

   • _____

   • _____

   • _____

   • _____

4. Practice your television interview with your partner and then present it to the class.

HEALTH CHALLENGE

List healthy salty and sweet foods you could eat next time you are tempted by junk food; e.g., a piece of cheese instead of potato chips; a peach instead of chocolate.

THE "PERFECT" BODY

Indicator

- Considers the types of people used in magazine advertisements.

Teacher information

- Teachers will need to provide a range of magazine advertisements featuring thin people. It is suggested that pairs of students choose one advertisement each to analyze for this activity. The answers to Question 4 could be used for a debate.

Additional activities

- Analyze television commercials for junk food. What kinds of people are used in these commercials? Are the commercials realistic?

- In small groups, design magazines that promote healthy eating and, exercise and use models with a range of healthy body types. This project could be extended over a number of weeks.

Answers

Answers will vary

The "Perfect" Body

Find a magazine advertisement that features people with "perfect" bodies. Analyze it using the headings below.

- This advertisement is for: _____

1. Describe the people/person in the advertisement.

   _____

   _____

   _____

   _____

   _____

2. Why do you think this type of person was used in this advertisement?

3. Imagine this advertisement is changed so it features a range of healthy body types. Would you be more or less likely to buy this product now? Explain.

   _____

   _____

   _____

   _____

   _____

   _____

   _____

4. "Advertisers should be forced by law to use a variety of healthy body types in advertisements." Write points "for" and "against" this statement.

For	Against

HEALTH CHALLENGE

Have ready-made healthy snacks in your fridge to snack on when you get hungry; e.g., carrot sticks, low-fat dips and cheese cubes .

NUTRITIONAL INFORMATION LABELS

Indicators

- Reads information about nutritional information on packaged food.

- Answers questions about nutritional information on packaged food.

Teacher information

- Federal and state laws require food manufacturers to accurately represent what their products contain. A nutritional information panel is displayed on the packaging of foods. This table usually lists the ingredients of the packaged food; the quantities per serving; the number of servings in the package; the number of calories; the levels of protein, the total grams of fat per serving, (including saturated fat); carbohydrates, sugar (both natural and added), dietary fiber, sodium (salt), and cholesterol.

- People use food nutritional panels for a number of reasons. It enables them to compare similar foods, allows them to select foods based on the nutritional content and to select the best foods for their diet and health.

- Read the information text with the students. They can then complete the questions independently. The answers could be discussed as a class.

Additional activities

- Create a nutritional panel for an unhealthy food that you think is fair and clear for customers.

- Use the Internet to find out how much sugar, fat, etc., is in your favorite packaged foods. Compare the results with other brands.

Answers

Answers will vary

Nutritional Information Labels

You will find nutritional information on most packaged food at the supermarket. Nutrients that must be specified according to government regulations include calories, protein, fat (total and saturated) and carbohydrates (total and sugars). Other nutrients such as dietary fiber or vitamins may also be listed.

Some food packages will also make claims like "reduced fat" or "low salt." This can help you to choose healthy food. However, you also need to be wary of this information.

"Reduced fat" does not necessarily mean the food is low in fat.

91% fat free means the food is 9% fat!

A food with less than 5 g of sugars, 3 g of fat and 120 mg of sodium (salt) per 100 grams is reasonably healthy.

Sugar, salt and fat can be called other names. For example, sugar can be listed as sucrose or dextrose; fat as lard or shortening; salt as sodium or soy sauce.

"Light" or "lite" may not mean the food is low in fat. It could mean it has a light color or taste!

The contents of the food is shown "per serving" and "per 100 g." It is better to look at the "100 g" column because the serving size may be more or less than what you would eat in one helping.

Choc Light
Reduced fat cookies
91% fat free
Nutritional information

Servings per package: 24
Serving size: 10.4 g (1 cookie)

	Per serving: 10.4 g	**Per 100 g**
Calories	240	1846
Protein	0.37 g	3.6 g
Fat, total	0.94 g	9 g
– saturated	0.31 g	3.1 g
Carbohydrates, total	8.5 g	83 g
– sugars	4.1 g	41 g
Dietary fiber	0.14 g	1.3 g
Sodium	40 mg	386 mg

1. Imagine that your parents have sent you to the supermarket to buy groceries. One of the items on their list is "healthy chocolate cookies."

   (a) Would you buy Choc Light cookies? ☐ YES ☐ NO

   (b) Explain your decision. _____

   _____

   _____

   _____

2. Name one other regulation you think should apply to nutritional information panels.

HEALTH CHALLENGE

Before you buy a packaged food at the supermarket, compare the fat, salt and sugar content of the different brands. You may be surprised at the difference!

FOOD LABEL INVESTIGATION

A HEALTHY DIET

Indicators

- Investigates the meanings of specific words and phrases found on a nutritional information label.
- States reasons for including specific information on a food label.

Teacher information

- Students will need a dictionary or access to the Internet for this activity.
- Students may work in pairs in order to share resources.
- Saturated fats are those which usually form a solid (or almost solid) state at room temperature. They include all animal fats, such as those found in meat, poultry and dairy products, processed and fast foods and sometimes vegetable oils. Examples of saturated fat vegetable oils include palm, palm kernel and coconut oils. Saturated fats are very unhealthy fats because they cause the body to produce more cholesterol which increases the risk of heart disease.
- Trans fats are a type of fat formed when liquid oils are made into solid fats such as shortening or hard margarine. They raise bad cholesterol (LDL) and increase the risk of heart disease. They may be found in foods such as vegetable shortenings, some margarines, crackers, candy, cookies, snack foods, fried and baked foods, and processed foods.

Additional activities

- Use the main headings from a nutritional information label to create an artwork using brightly colored markers, crayons, or pencils.
- Collect food panels or labels which have misleading information on them such as "lite"/ "light," "low fat" (high sugar).
- Brainstorm to list other suggestions for inclusions on a food panel.

Answers

Teacher check. Note: the majority of these answers may be found in the glossary on pages ix-xiii. Only "saturated fat" and "trans fat" will need Internet research.

Food Label Investigation

Nutrition Facts	
Serving Size 1 cup (230g)	
Servings Per Container 2	

Amount Per Serving

Calories 200 — Calories from Fat 10

	% **Daily Value**
Total Fat 10 g	**18%**
Saturated Fat 4 g	**15%**
Trans Fat 2 g	
Cholesterol 20 mg	**10%**
Sodium 450 mg	**20%**
Total Carbohydrate 30 g	**10%**
Dietary Fiber 0 g	
Sugars 4 g	
Protein 6 g	**4%**
Vitamin A	**2%**
Vitamin C	**20%**
Calcium	**4%**
Iron	

* Percent Daily Value are based on a 2,000 calorie diet. Your Daily Values may be higher or lower depending on your calorie needs.

	Calories:	2,000	2,500
Total Fat	Less than	65 g	80 g
Sat Fat	Less than	20 g	25 g
Cholesterol	Less than	300 g	300 mg
Sodium	Less than	2,400m	2,400 mg
Total Carbohydrate		300 g	375 g
Dietary Fiber		25 g	30 g

1. Use a dictionary or the Internet to find the meanings of the following words or phrases:

(a) nutrition: _____

_____

(b) calorie: _____

_____

(c) saturated fat: _____

_____

(d) trans fat: _____

_____

_____

(e) cholesterol: _____

_____

(f) sodium: _____

_____

(g) carbohydrate: _____

_____

_____

(h) dietary fiber: _____

_____

_____

(i) sugar: _____

_____

(j) protein: _____

_____

2. Give reasons for including

(a) Vitamin A, Vitamin C, calcium and iron: _____

_____

(b) percent daily values: _____

_____

JUNK FOOD

Indicators

- Reads a newspaper article about junk food.
- Answers questions about junk food.

Teacher information

- Childhood obesity is increasing at an alarming rate. One third of children may be classified as overweight. The average daily intake of food per child has increased. Children who are overweight are at serious risk of developing health problems in later life. These include heart disease caused by raised blood pressure, blood cholesterol and blood sugar, and also type 2 diabetes. Overweight children have a 50% chance of becoming overweight adults. Children of overweight parents have twice the risk of being overweight as adults.

- Busy working parents are depending more and more on junk food as a means to feed families.

- Junk food can be classified as food which has little nutritional value. Most junk foods are high in sugar, fats and calories, may contain a lot of artificial flavors and additives, and have very few nutrients.

- Nobody expects children or adults to always eat healthy food. There is a great variety of foods for us to sample and enjoy. Junk food should be considered "treats" and only eaten occasionally.

- Read the information text with the students. They can then complete the questions independently.

Note: The risk of developing Type 2 diabetes can be lessened by maintaining a healthy lifestyle. Type 1 diabetes is hereditary and cannot be prevented.

Additional activities

- Prepare and deliver a speech as a nutritional expert that explains why junk food is so bad for people. Students may need to do some additional research to find some appropriate statistics.

- Design a healthy fast food restaurant. It should appeal to all ages. Think about colors, displays, menu items, promotional giveaways with meals, etc.

Answers

1. Answers will vary
2. They are high in saturated fat and salt.
3. Answers will vary

©World Teachers Press®

Junk Food

The Daily Herald June 25, 2005

"Cut back on junk food," says expert

The amount of junk food consumed by Americans is a fast-growing problem. Foods with little nutritional value, like soft drinks, cookies, potato chips, hamburgers and fried chicken, are now becoming a part of our daily diets.

"We are now spending about one-third of our household budget on junk-food meals," says nutritional expert Dr. Laura George. "This is usually blamed on the busy lifestyles of today's families. But unfortunately, junk food is contributing to the increase in the rate of heart disease, childhood obesity, high cholesterol levels and other serious health problems."

Dr. George says that the average person should eat less than 20 grams of saturated fat a day. But just one fast food meal can have this amount and more! Fast food also has an alarmingly high level of salt. Too much salt in our diet can cause high blood pressure, which in turn contributes to heart disease.

And all those sugary foods you love are not doing you any favors either. Too much sugar is thought to contribute to obesity. But don't feel that you can't eat junk food ever again—just keep it to the occasional treat.

"And if you must eat fast food," says Dr. George, "try healthier options like vegetarian pizza or skinless chicken. Remember, too, that you can make quick and easy, healthy meals at home, like homemade hamburgers with oven fries—these are far healthier than the takeout versions."

1. How much of a household budget do you think should be spent on fast or junk food? Give reasons for your answer.

   _____

   _____

2. Write one problem with fast food meals.

   _____

3. Use the text and your own ideas to list some healthy but tasty alternatives to these junk foods.

super supreme pizza	
fried chicken	
french fries	
a chocolate bar	
soft drink	

HEALTH CHALLENGE

Try making healthy hamburgers at home using lean ground beef, flat bread and loads of lettuce.

HEALTHY FOOD PACKAGING

A HEALTHY DIET

Indicator

- Designs healthy food packaging based on appealing fast food designs.

Teacher information

- Teachers will need to collect a range of fast food packaging for this activity—the students could help with this. Three or four examples should be placed on each student's desk for visual reference.

- Read the information text at the top of the page with the students. They can then complete Question 1 and discuss the answers with the class. Questions 2 and 3 can be completed independently. The students will require thin cardstock or paper to complete Question 3. Display the students' designs in the classroom.

Additional activities

- Write a list of some things that fast food restaurants do to encourage you to visit them and eat more; e.g., promotional "giveaways," "meal deals."

- Write what you think might happen if fast food restaurants were outlawed in the United States.

Answers

Answers will vary

Healthy Food Packaging

Imagine you are opening a healthy fast food restaurant. You decide to design a style of fast food packaging that will help make your products more appealing to your customers.

Look at some simple fast food packaging from fast food chains, such as hamburger wrappers, french fry bags and boxes for fried chicken.

1. Describe the types of colors, patterns and writing used on these.

    _____

    _____

    _____

    _____

2. Decide on two healthy items you could sell at your new restaurant. For each, draw a labeled diagram to show how you want the packaging to look, based on your junk food research.

    Item 1 _____   Item 2 _____

HEALTH CHALLENGE

Next time you are at a fast food restaurant that offers "healthier" alternatives to its regular products, find out what the differences in the fat, salt and sugar content really are.

3. Use paper or cardstock to create your designs. You can use the fast food containers to help you. Decorate your packaging with colored pencils or markers.

43
HEALTHY CHOICES

WHAT IS EXERCISE?

EXERCISE AND FITNESS

Indicators

- Understands what exercise does for the body.
- Appreciates there are different types of exercise.

Teacher information

- Different exercises strengthen different parts of the body.

  The body can be broadly divided into three parts:
  - the cardiovascular system (heart and blood vessels)
  - the arms and upper body (shoulders and chest)
  - the legs and lower body (abdomen and lower back)

- Different parts of the body are exercised during different sports. For example, in cycling, the cardiovascular system, legs and lower body are exercised. A cyclist may have a small upper body and arms by comparison. Many athletes cross train to compensate for this difference. This means, they exercise in another sport or discipline to train the part which receives less exercise in the main sport.

- The body has two systems for producing energy for exercise, aerobic and anaerobic. The aerobic system uses oxygen to produce energy. The anaerobic system produces energy without oxygen. In most cases, a combination of the two systems is used during exercise. Only very easy work is completely aerobic and only very short explosive work is completely anaerobic. The mixture of the two systems depends on your work rate and fitness level.

- If the level of effort during exercise is less than the body is used to, fitness will be reduced. If it is the same, fitness will be maintained. If it greater, fitness will be increased.

- For children, the emphasis is on enjoying a wide range of activities to provide a balance in exercise for all parts of the body. It is not necessary to belong to sports organizations to achieve the required amount of exercise. Playing in the park, climbing on the playground equipment, or running and playing ball games, provides plenty of exercise.

- Read and discuss the information with the students before asking them to complete the questions independently.

Additional activities

- Make a poster of exercise words and pictures.
- Students record the exercise they do for one week. Can they improve on this? Make a realistic plan for one week's exercise, with a minimum of 30 minutes each day.
- Plan a survey to investigate how much exercise students in the class take each week.

Answers

1. (a) Exercise trains and improves the body, making the heart, lungs and muscles strong.

   (b) rowing, swimming

   (c) hand-eye or foot-eye coordination, whole body coordination, balance, flexibility

2. (a) false (b) true (c) false

3. (a) skipping (b) walking (c) surfing (d) gardening

4. Teacher check

What Is Exercise?

Exercise is something we do to train and improve the body, making the heart, lungs and muscles strong, allowing us to perform at our best.

Forms of exercise such as cycling and running train only certain parts of the body. Others such as rowing and swimming give the body a complete workout. Exercise also improves skills. For example, ball games such as soccer and tennis improve foot-eye or hand-eye coordination, while dance and gymnastics improve whole body coordination, balance and flexibility.

To be healthy and enjoy life, we need to exercise. We don't have to think of ourselves as athletes to enjoy exercise. Walking, riding a bike, gardening, skateboarding, roller skating, housework, surfing and skipping are all forms of exercise that train and improve our bodies.

There are two types of exercise:

- *Aerobic – Those which can be done over a long period of time, such as swimming, walking and jogging.*
- *Anaerobic – Those which use a short burst of explosive effort, such as tennis serves, short sprints and weight-lifting.*

Answer these questions.

1. (a) What does exercise do for the body?

   _____

   _____

   (b) List two exercises which give a complete workout for the body.

   (i) _____ (ii) _____

   (c) List two skills which can be improved with exercise.

   (i) _____

   (ii) _____

2. True or false?

   (a) Only athletes need to exercise.　　　　　　　　　　　　| TRUE | FALSE |

   (b) Gardening and housework are forms of exercise.　　　| TRUE | FALSE |

   (c) Exercise that takes a lot of hard effort can be done for a long time.　| TRUE | FALSE |

3. Rearrange the letters to find types of exercise.

   (a) pgsnpiik   (b) knawlig

   _____   _____

   (c) fgunris   (d) dringgaen

   _____   _____

4. What exercise do you, or would you like to, take part in? Explain why.

HEALTH CHALLENGE

Try to fit in at least 30 minutes of exercise each day.

WHAT HAPPENS DURING EXERCISE?

EXERCISE AND FITNESS

Indicators

- Recognizes the symptoms the body experiences during and after exercise.
- Understands why these symptoms occur.

Teacher information

- Sweating is the body's mechanism for cooling down from the heat produced during exercise. The fluid lost through sweating must be replaced to prevent dehydration, which can, in extreme cases, cause serious health problems. Students should be encouraged to drink frequent, small quantities of water during exercise rather than waiting until they feel thirsty. As soon as the body starts to dehydrate, there is a decrease in performance level. To maintain peak condition during exercise, water needs to be consumed.

- Aching muscles can occur if too much exercise is done too soon at a rate that is too hard for the body in its current state.

- Warming up with gentle exercise can prevent injuries and tears to muscles. Stretching muscles after warming up prepares them for the exercise ahead.

- Cooling down with gentle exercise and stretches releases the build up of lactic acid in the blood which can cause cramps and painful knots in the muscles.

- Read and discuss the information text with the students before asking them to complete the crossword independently or in pairs.

Additional activities

- Design a poster showing which parts of the body are exercised during different exercises. In skipping, for example, the heart, lungs and leg muscles are exercised a lot and the arms a little.

- Design an "Exercise" board game. Give "throw again" and "go forward" chances for good practices such as drinking enough water, warming up correctly, walking to school. Give "go back" and "miss a turn" forfeits for bad practices such as "watching too much TV," "drinking soft drinks instead of water," "not stretching before exercise," "not getting enough rest."

- With a partner, research the working of the heart. Draw a picture showing the four chambers and the main blood vessels leading to and from the heart. Show which vessels go to and from the lungs and to and from the rest of the body.

Answers

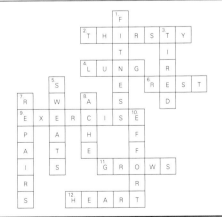

www.worldteacherspress.com   ©World Teachers Press®

What Happens During Exercise?

Playing with friends, going on outings to a park, beach, or playground all give us plenty of exercise. Our body lets us know when it has worked hard. Do you recognize any of these symptoms?

- *sweating*
- *feeling thirsty*
- *feeling tired*
- *aching muscles*

When we put effort into exercise, changes occur within the body which improve fitness.

During aerobic exercise, the lungs take in more air and so more oxygen passes into the blood. The heart beats faster, pumping more blood around the body so the muscles can work harder and become stronger.

Sweating is the body's way of cooling down from the heat produced during exercise. We should drink plenty of water during exercise to make up for what we lose when we sweat. Feeling thirsty is the body's way of telling us it needs more water.

After exercise, we may feel tired and have aching muscles. This is because the body has been asked to work hard. The body likes hard work because it increases its fitness, but it also needs plenty of rest so that it can repair and grow.

Rest is a very important part of exercise!

Use the information in the text to complete the crossword.

Across

2. How you feel when the body needs water.

4. From each _____, oxygen passes into the blood.

6. You need this after exercise.

9. You do this to keep active.

11. The body does this while you rest.

12. The muscle which pumps blood around the body.

Down

1. Hard exercise increases this.

3. The body feels like this after exercise.

5. The body does this to cool down.

7. The body does this while you rest.

8. You may do this after exercise.

10. This is needed to increase fitness.

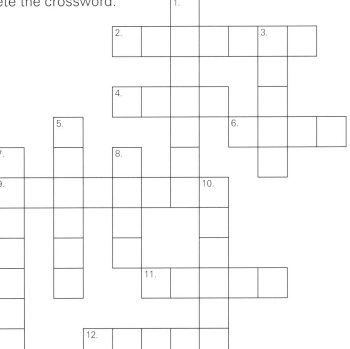

HEALTH CHALLENGE

For 20 minutes each day, exercise hard enough to sweat and feel thirsty.

WHAT ARE THE BENEFITS OF EXERCISE?

EXERCISE AND FITNESS

Indicators

• Learns what happens to the body during exercise.

• Recognizes the body parts affected during exercise.

Teacher information

• In addition to the physical benefits described on the worksheet, there are other reasons why exercise is good for you. The feeling of well-being created cannot be underestimated.

• For students to gain the greatest confidence in their achievements, their personal goals and expectations must be realistic, the atmosphere must be positive and supportive, and the emphasis must be on enjoyment.

• If all these factors are present, students are more likely to continue with exercise for a healthy lifestyle.

• Read and discuss the information text and diagram with the students before asking them to complete the tasks independently.

Additional activities

• With a partner, sketch an outline of a body. Research the location of the main muscle groups. Draw and label them on the body. Write a list of activities which exercise each muscle group. Attach this list to each muscle group. Display body pictures.

• Make a list of six of the main muscle groups in the body and where they are located; e.g., biceps/upper arm (front), triceps/upper arm (back), gastrocnemius/lower leg (back), gluteus maximas/bottom, deltoids/shoulders, trapezius/head, shoulders. Make up 12 playing cards with the name of a muscle group or body part on each. Shuffle them well and play games such as Snap and Concentration, matching the muscle group with the correct body part.

• With a partner, plan activities that could be enjoyed by both families spending an afternoon at the beach or park. Plan for about two hours. List any equipment needed. Estimate how long each activity might take. (Not everyone has to be included in all activities.)

Answers

1. Teacher check

2. (a) false   (b) true   (c) false   (d) true   (e) true

What Are the Benefits of Exercise?

Exercise improves the body in many ways.

- *The lungs take in more air, giving us more oxygen.*
- *The heart works harder to get more blood and oxygen to the parts of the body that are working.*
- *The heart and muscles become larger, stronger and fitter.*
- *Weight-bearing exercises like running, skipping and hopping help to develop strong bones.*
- *Food is processed more efficiently and waste products are more quickly removed, leaving the body feeling more comfortable.*
- *The skin, hair and eyes look better because the "inside" is healthy.*
- *Improved muscle tone gives the body a better shape and posture.*
- *Chemicals are released into the brain which make us feel happy. These are called endorphins. They make us feel more confident and improve our self-esteem.*
- *We sleep better.*
- *Strength, stamina and suppleness are improved.*

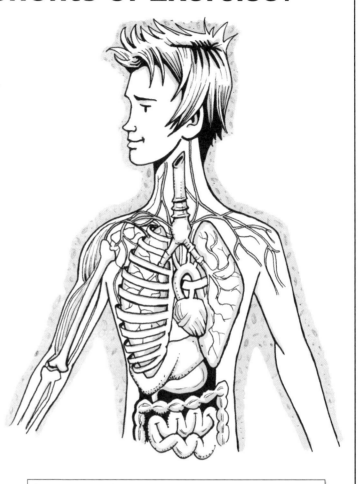

heart, muscles, bones, stomach, intestines, skin, hair, eyes, lungs, blood vessels

Complete these activities.

1. Label the diagram of the body using words from the word bank.

2. Circle true or false.

   (a) The body needs less oxygen when we exercise. | TRUE | FALSE |

   (b) Endorphins make us feel good. | TRUE | FALSE |

   (c) Muscles become smaller when exercised. | TRUE | FALSE |

   (d) Weight-bearing exercise develops strong bones. | TRUE | FALSE |

   (e) The digestive system improves with exercise. | TRUE | FALSE |

HEALTH CHALLENGE

With a small group of friends, plan six fun activities for a 30-minute exercise session. Do them as a circuit, with each person starting on a different one. Every three minutes, move to the next one. Keep going until the 30 minutes is up.

EXERCISING WITH A GROUP

EXERCISE AND FITNESS

Indicators

- Appreciates the benefits of belonging to a sports team.
- Considers options for joining a sports team.

Teacher information

- At this stage, most students will be enjoying physical exercise for its own sake and only some will have distant dreams of careers as professional athletes. A broad choice of activities, enjoyed in an atmosphere of friendship and fun, will promote the notion that exercise is a social activity and something to be continued through life.

- Organized sports for this age group should still be conducted as a social activity but with the introduction of life skills such as commitment and responsibility. Attendance at training sessions, availability for competition and appreciation of other team members are important.

- Students will learn to appreciate the social and health benefits of physical activity with a group. With an increasing number of friends, they will see it as a more enjoyable and productive way of spending leisure time than indulging exclusively in passive activities such as watching TV.

- Read and discuss the information text before asking students to complete the questions independently.

Additional activities

- Organize an exercise club. Give the club a name. Decide on the aims of the club. Does the club have a motto? Plan activities and timetables for training sessions. Advertise for members.

- Invent a team game using skills and equipment from any number of games you already know. Record the rules, method of scoring, time played, equipment required, etc. Ask a friend to check through your ideas, then try the game with other members of the class.

- Survey the class to determine how many students take part in organized sports.

Answers

1. Answers may include enjoying traveling to different venues for competitions, learning to accept defeat as well as enjoying triumphs, or having specific goals to help with motivation.

2. Teacher check

3. (a) soccer   (b) gymnastics   (c) tennis   (d) cycling   (e) dancing   (f) swimming

Exercising with a Group

Being active with friends and family can be great fun, but joining with a more formal group has extra advantages.

- *You can join a team of your preferred activity and focus on developing skills and techniques for that activity.*

- *Coaches and teachers have a good understanding and knowledge of the activity and can guide you if you wish to progress to higher levels in the sport.*

- *You learn commitment, which is an important life skill. This happens in a number of ways:*
  - *You agree to attend training sessions and to take part in the activities organized by the teachers and coaches.*
  - *As part of a team, you learn to rely on one another so it is important not to let anyone down by "giving up."*

- *Working with others improves motivation as it is more fun than doing things on your own.*

- *You meet new friends with similar interests.*

Answer these questions.

1. What is another benefit for joining a team?

   _____

   _____

2. Choose an activity in which you would like to participate.

Activity:

   (a) What equipment is required for this activity?

   _____

   (b) What exercise is involved? (e.g., running, kicking, jumping, twisting, rolling)

   _____

   (c) Briefly explain why you have chosen this activity.

3. Match the activity to the description.

(a)	round ball invasion game played on a field •	• dancing
(b)	whole body movement on apparatus •	• cycling
(c)	racquet and ball game played on a court divided by a net •	• soccer
(d)	requires a two-wheeled machine and a helmet •	• swimming
(e)	whole body movement with music •	• tennis
(f)	requires a safe water environment •	• gymnastics

HEALTH CHALLENGE

Make a commitment with a friend to exercise regularly. Plan the days and time and keep to it.

HEALTHY CHOICES

WHAT IS FITNESS?

Indicators

- Understands the term "fitness" with respect to pulse rate.

- Learns how to take own pulse and calculate pulse rate.

Teacher information

- Fitness is a measure of good health and physical condition. Serious athletes who train for an average of eight hours a day are in peak condition and training to their full potential. For the majority of people, fitness means being physically capable of doing all the things they want to do.

- Pulse rate is recognized as being an accurate indicator of fitness. The faster the pulse rate rises during exercise and the faster it returns to normal are signs of a fit body. Exercising within an individual's training heart rate range produces the greatest training effect. Below this level, the body is not working hard enough to improve fitness.

- For an accurate measure of resting pulse, the body needs to be at rest and relaxed for at least 15 minutes before measurement is taken. Let students practice taking their pulse before they are required to measure their resting pulse. This may then be done after a quiet period, such as silent reading time.

- Read and discuss the information text at the top of the worksheet with the students. Work through the step-by-step instructions for measuring the resting pulse with the students, who record personal pulse rates. The teacher can hold a stopwatch and count the 15 seconds required or a clock with a second hand could be displayed.

- To discover "How fit am I?" students need to follow the exercises outlined on the worksheet. Plastic cones or markers and stopwatches will be required.

- In pairs, the students work through the sequence of warm-up, hard exercise and pulse reading to determine the time taken for their pulse rate to return to normal. (Be sensitive as to the pairings of students.)

- When all students have their results, they can make a rough assessment of their own fitness and consider how they might work to improve.

- It would be preferable not to compare students with one another as there may be students with serious health issues. Encourage the notion that the only comparison should be "How fit am I now?" with "How fit will I be after a period of regular exercise?"

Additional activities

- Students start a diary and record their resting pulse rate each week for one semester. Remember to take it after resting. Show the change over time on a graph.

- Produce a poem or piece of writing describing how they feel about having a healthy lifestyle. Include the triumphs and failures they have experienced in their quest for good health.

- Interview someone they know who has increased their fitness and improved their life by taking up sports.

Answers

Teacher check

EXERCISE AND FITNESS

What Is Fitness?

Fitness is described as how easily we can do a physical activity and how quickly the body recovers afterwards. Your pulse rate is an indication of how fit you are. Pulse rate is measured by the number of times the heart beats in one minute. When we exercise, the heart pumps faster to deliver blood more quickly to the parts of the body that need it. During exercise, our pulse rate is higher than when we are resting. To measure fitness, the pulse is taken immediately after exercise and then every minute until it returns to the normal resting pulse. The fitter you are, the faster you recover.

How to find and measure your pulse:

1. Follow the instructions to find your resting pulse.

    * Using the pads of the middle and index fingers of either hand, locate your pulse on your neck, below the jawline, on either side of the wind-pipe. You will be able to feel it throbbing.

    * Practice counting each beat.

    * Using a stopwatch, count how many times your pulse beats over 15 seconds.

    * Multiply this figure by four to give your pulse rate. The normal resting pulse rate for children from the age of ten and adults is between 60 and 100 beats per minute (bpm). The best time to take your resting pulse is when you are really relaxed.

    * My pulse rate is: _____ x 4 = _____ bpm

How fit am I?

2. Follow the instructions to find your pulse rate after exercise.

    * Jog for at least five minutes to warm up and do some gentle stretching to prepare your body for exercise.

    * For five minutes, run hard between two cones set 15 yards apart. Each time you reach a cone, bend down and touch the ground.

    * After five minutes, start taking your pulse. This time, do it for ten seconds and multiply the figure by six. Wait for 50 seconds before doing it again. Keep measuring until your rate has returned to normal. Work with a partner. Call out the number of pulses you count and your partner will write it down and calculate your rate.

0 minutes: _____ x 6 = _____ bpm	5 minutes: _____ x 6 = _____ bpm
1 minute: _____ x 6 = _____ bpm	6 minutes: _____ x 6 = _____ bpm
2 minutes: _____ x 6 = _____ bpm	7 minutes: _____ x 6 = _____ bpm
3 minutes: _____ x 6 = _____ bpm	8 minutes: _____ x 6 = _____ bpm
4 minutes: _____ x 6 = _____ bpm	9 minutes: _____ x 6 = _____ bpm

3. It took _____ minutes for my pulse rate to return to normal.

HEALTH CHALLENGE

Each week, measure how long it takes for your pulse to return to normal after exercise. Are you getting fitter?

PLANNING A DAILY FITNESS ROUTINE

Indicators

- Appreciates that improving fitness requires regular, sustained effort.
- Designs a personal fitness routine.

Teacher information

- Read through the text to promote discussion before asking students to plan their routine.

- Explain that fitness comes with regular sustained effort and that results will be seen over time rather than immediately. Students might like to keep a diary of what they actually achieved each day, and where relevant, record times, distances, or number of repetitions. After a period of time, they can compare their current results with their original results to see how they have improved.

- Working with a partner will help with motivation. Quite often, the times we feel least like exercising are the times we perform the best. Having a training partner encourages us to do the session when we would prefer to miss it. It is important that partners are of similar physical ability or that the activities planned cater to different abilities. For example, running around a track would require the pair to be of a similar standard, whereas working within the same area doing star jumps, squat thrusts and shuttle runs would enable each student to work at his/her own level while remaining in the same place.

- It is vital that the routines are realistic and achievable so they can be maintained. Above all, they must be fun. At this stage, students should be thinking about how exercise enhances their enjoyment of life.

Additional activities

- Plan a daily fitness routine that can be enjoyed by the whole family.
- Research their favorite sport, listing the skills required to play it. Plan a fitness routine that includes practicing these skills.
- Interview someone they know who trains with a team. Find out the amount and variety of training they do each week.

Answers

Teacher check

Planning a Daily Fitness Routine

Fitness can only be improved over a period of time during which we regularly make our bodies work hard enough for our pulse rate to rise. For a fitness routine to work, it needs to be planned so that it fits easily into daily life.

Let's begin!

Exercising with a partner helps to keep you motivated, so find a friend!

1. My training buddy is _____.

2. With your buddy, plan your fitness routine.

   (a) Discuss when you are going to do your routine. It may be at school or after school and may be at a different time each day. (30 minutes each day is the minimum recommended amount of time for exercise.) You will need to consider any other commitments you already have.

   (b) What are you going to do? Remember that varying your routine will keep it interesting. Choose activities you enjoy. Before you begin your session, remember to warm up and stretch to prepare your body for exercising. When you have finished, cool down by exercising gently. Drink plenty of water.

   Your 30-minute session might look like this.

5 minutes:	warm up and stretch	breathing normally
10 minutes:	gradual build up of effort	breathing a little harder
5 minutes:	really hard effort	breathing hard
5 minutes:	gradual slow down	breathing a little easier
5 minutes:	gentle exercise	breathing normally

3. Fill in this fitness chart, briefly describing what you will do.

	Time	Activity	Description
Monday			
Tuesday			
Wednesday			
Thursday			
Friday			
Saturday			
Sunday			

HEALTH CHALLENGE

As you get more fit, increase your hard effort from five to seven minutes and reduce the build up from ten to eight minutes.

ATHLETE PERSONALITY PROFILE

EXERCISE AND FITNESS

Indicators

- Chooses an athlete as a role model.
- Researches the achievements of the chosen role model.

Teacher information

- Students will need to have access to the Internet to research the achievements of their chosen athlete. They could also try to locate past and present newspaper and magazine articles.

- While admiring the successes of their role models on the world stage, the students must be reminded that their own personal endeavors and achievements are more important. Being actively involved in improving their own fitness and well-being is the best way they can emulate their sporting heroes.

- Many professional athletes have chosen to be associated with schools in an effort to encourage students to take exercise and sports more seriously. They are using their high public profile in a positive way by giving back to schools and clubs some of the help they had when they were beginning in the sport.

Additional activities

- Make a "Sporting heroes" collage of American athletes.
- Design a poster of their chosen athlete. Use pictures and headlines from magazines and newspapers. Display the poster in class.

Answers

Teacher check

Athlete Profile

Today, many athletes have high public profiles. They receive a lot of media attention and many things about their private and professional lives are common knowledge.

1. Choose an athlete you admire and complete the profile.

Name:	
Sport:	Number of years playing sport:
Records held:	
Greatest achievements:	
Major competitions:	

2. Why do you admire this athlete?

_____

_____

_____

3. Do you participate in this athlete's sport?   YES   NO

4. Would you like to become a professional athlete?   YES   NO

5. What qualities does someone need to become a professional athlete?

_____

_____

_____

HEALTH CHALLENGE

Use the dedication professional athletes have for their sports to motivate you when you exercise.

IAN THORPE –
AN AUSTRALIAN SPORTING LEGEND

EXERCISE AND FITNESS

Indicators

- Learns about the sporting achievements of Ian Thorpe.
- Appreciates that successful athletes start working on their skills and fitness at an early age.

Teacher information

- The main purpose of looking at a celebrity is to demonstrate the possible achievements of ordinary people. We all have opportunities, but what is important is whether we make use of them or not.

- While it is good to have a celebrity as a positive role model, the students must still realize that this person is just an ordinary human being who has reached his or her present position through hard work and determination. We can't all be Olympic athletes, but we can all aspire to do and be the best we can.

- Students know that people are all different. What is easy to achieve for one person may be a major challenge for another. They must learn to respect the efforts of everyone, including themselves, and not unfairly compare one person with another.

- Read and discuss Ian Thorpe's profile with the students before they answer the questions independently.

Additional activities

- Choose either the men's or women's competition in any sport in the most recent Olympic Games, or World Championships. Research to find the gold, silver and bronze medalists in each event. Include their nationalities. From the data collected, note the most successful athletes and their countries of origin. Write a brief summary to share with the class.

- Research the sporting achievements of students in the class. Design a class "Roll of Honor" to display in the room.

- In 2000, Ian Thorpe was named "Young Australian of the Year" for his services to sports and his support of charities. Think of an award to bestow on someone in the class. Decide who students believe deserves the award. Give reasons for their choice.

Answers

1. 15 years
2. "Thorpedo" is a play on Ian's name, "Thorpe," and "torpedo," which is an explosive missile fired from submarines.
3. He donated $25,000 to charity.
4. Answers may include:

   Sydney Olympics, 2000 – three gold medals, two silver medals

   Athens Olympics, 2004 – two gold medals, one silver medal, one bronze medal

   World Championships, Perth, 1998 – one gold medal

   Commonwealth Games, Kuala Lumpur, 1998 – four gold medals

5. He likes to go surfing, to the movies and play computer games.

Ian Thorpe –
An Australian Sporting Legend

Everyone knows the name and face of Ian Thorpe, one of Australia's most famous and successful swimmers. He is recognized at the pool as the tall athlete with big feet and a wide smile, wearing the full body suit.

By the age of 21, Ian had already competed in two Olympic Games. In Sydney 2000, he won three gold and two silver medals, and in Athens 2004, he won two gold, one silver and one bronze medal.

Ian Thorpe's first major title came in 1998 when he was just 15 years old. He won a gold medal in the 400m freestyle at the World Championships in Perth. Seven months later, at the Commonwealth Games in Kuala Lumpur, he won four gold medals. After this success, he was given the name "Thorpedo."

At the 2001 World Championships, Ian won six gold medals, four of them in world record times.

In 1999, Ian won $25,000 for setting the first world record in the newly-built Sydney Olympic Pool. He donated all the money to Lifeline and the Children's Cancer Institute of Australia.

Ian started competitive swimming when he was eight years old. At 14, he became the youngest male swimmer ever to be selected for the national swimming squad.

His favorite hobbies include surfing, computer games and going to the movies.

Answer these questions.

1. How old was Ian when he won his first gold medal? _____

2. Why do you think Ian was given the name "Thorpedo"?

    _____

3. What evidence in the text suggests that Ian Thorpe is a generous person?

    _____

4. Ian Thorpe has achieved phenomenal success in his sports career. Give three examples of his great achievements.

①	②	③

5. Ian Thorpe may be a sports legend but he is still human and needs to balance his lifestyle. What does he like to do to relax?

    _____

    _____

HEALTH CHALLENGE

When Ian Thorpe started competitive swimming at the age of eight, he did not know how successful he was going to be. He just always did his best. Do your best with everything you try. Who knows where it may lead!

HEALTHY CHOICES

COMMUNITY SPORTS FACILITIES

Indicators

- Learns about the community sports facilities available in the local area.
- Considers which of these facilities he/she might use.

Teacher information

- Students will need access to local maps to locate their school and to be informed of the street boundaries within which they will be looking for local community sports facilities.
- Teachers and students can collect programs from community centers in the area or research on the Internet to ascertain the sports provided for at each one.
- Students place a tally mark each time they find a venue for each sport listed in the table on the worksheet.
- While there are many sports facilities available to us, it may not be practical for students and their families to make use of them. However, by promoting an awareness and interest in them, it may be possible for some logistical problems to be overcome; for example, ride sharing to venues so parents aren't committed every week.
- A whole-school survey of sports facilities used by students and which activities they enjoy might result in more students taking part.

Additional activities

- Survey the class to determine what use is made of local parks for both organized sports and recreation.
- Using the community newspaper as a resource, follow the fortunes of a local sports team. Contact the team for a games schedule and latest results.
- Survey the class to determine how many parents are actively involved in sports.

Answers

Teacher check

Community Sports Facilities

Local councils provide and maintain facilities for a number of sporting activities. For example:

- *aquatic centers   – for swimming, diving, water polo*
- *outdoor facilities – for football, baseball, hockey, tennis, lacrosse*
- *indoor facilities   – for squash, basketball*

There are also many clubs which require the participant to pay an annual or term membership fee; for example, squash, tennis, rowing, gymnastics and dancing.

Where are your local sports facilities?

1. Using resources such as your own and other people's knowledge, directories and local newspapers, find local venues where you might be able to enjoy the following sports. Add four of your own choice in the blank boxes. Add a tally mark each time you find a venue for each sport.

	Tally	Total		Tally	Total
swimming			baseball		
dancing			squash		
gymnastics			tennis		
football			athletics		
soccer			rugby		
basketball			lacrosse		

2. Which of these sports has the most facilities available? _____

3. Are there sports not mentioned in the table which are provided for in your local community? List them here.

    _____

    _____

4. Which sports would you be able to participate in if you.

    (a) Were only able to walk to the venue?

        _____

        _____

    (b) Could take public transportation?

        _____

        _____

HEALTH CHALLENGE

Select and regularly use the facilities provided by your local community.

MY LOCAL RECREATION CENTER

Indicators

- Considers that community facilities are a valuable resource for many people.
- Considers the loss that would be felt by a range of people if a center was closed down.

Teacher information

- Students will need to be aware of patrons of all ages who use community centers and what facilities are available to them. A copy of the local center's program, a visit from the manager, or a letter requesting information would facilitate this.
- In considering why their center should remain open, they will need to empathize with the members of each group and ask themselves how the center's closure would affect these people. This could be conducted as an activity where the class is divided into groups, with each one representing a group at the recreation center.

Additional activities

- Survey the class to determine how many students attended sports lessons before they started school; for example, swimming, gymnastics, dancing.
- Make up a directory of local sport centers and the activities that are provided in each.
- Design a "Use your local center" poster.

Answers

Teacher check

EXERCISE AND FITNESS

My Local Recreation Center

Recreation centers provide sporting facilities for people of all ages, from babies taking infant swimming lessons to seniors enjoying water aerobics. For many people working towards a healthier lifestyle, using these facilities has become a regular part of their lives.

Imagine that one day, each visitor to your local center receives the following letter from the center's management.

Dear patron:

Due to a lack of city council funds for sports and recreation, one of the local centers must be closed down. Please show your support for this center by completing the information sheet for our center and sending it to the council.

Yours faithfully, The manager

Name of center: *New Town Recreation Center*

Hours of operation:
Monday – Friday: *10:00 a.m. – 5:00 p.m.*   Saturday – Sunday: *8:00 a.m. – 5:00 p.m.*

Days and time(s) you attend:

Sports you participate in:

Fitness classes you participate in:

Leisure activities you participate in:

Number of adults in your family using this center:

Number of children in your family using this center:

I think this center should remain open because:

HEALTH CHALLENGE

Choose an activity that your whole family can regularly enjoy at your local center and try it.

FINDING THE BALANCE

SELF-MANAGEMENT

Indicators

- Reads information about a balanced lifestyle.
- Answers questions about a balanced lifestyle.

Teacher information

- Following a healthy diet, getting regular exercise, adequate sleep, and balancing the demands of work and school with relaxation help to provide a balanced, healthy lifestyle. More emphasis on one area while neglecting another causes stress, poor health and the inability to cope with the demands of daily life.

- Read and discuss the information text with the students. They can then complete the questions independently.

Additional activities

- Students list small jobs they can do at home to help parents have a few extra minutes of relaxation time. Students can select one of these to carry out for a week as a gift for a birthday, Father's Day, Mother's Day, or simply as a kind deed.

- Students create colorful posters using the four main aspects of a balanced lifestyle—diet, exercise, sleep and relaxation.

- Discuss the possible bad effects of putting more emphasis on one area of life than another; for example, stress, short temper, inability to sleep or relax, headaches, health problems.

Answers

1. household chores, homework, sports and leisure activities, family activities, socializing with friends
2. balanced lifestyle
3. eating a healthy diet, getting regular exercise, getting enough sleep, relaxation
4. Teacher check

Finding the Balance

- *Life today can be very busy for both adults and children. There are a lot of demands upon our time from family, school, work and friends.*

- *Children may have household chores to do, homework to complete, sports and leisure activities after school and on the weekend, family activities and social activities, such as visiting friends. Adults often find themselves putting more emphasis on one area of their life than another. They may spend many hours working and less time relaxing or with their families. This can have a damaging effect on their health.*

- *A person who has a balanced lifestyle is better able to cope with the demands of a busy life.*

- *The four most important aspects of a balanced lifestyle include:*
  - *eating a healthy diet*   – *getting regular exercise*
  - *getting enough sleep*   – *finding enough time for relaxation*

Answer these questions.

1. Give five reasons why children may have a busy lifestyle.
    - _____
    - _____
    - _____
    - _____
    - _____

2. Complete the sentence.
    A person who has a _____ is better able to cope with the demands of a busy life.

3. List the four most important aspects of a balanced lifestyle.
    - _____
    - _____
    - _____
    - _____

4. Give one reason why it may be difficult for some adults, such as those who work long hours, to balance their lifestyle.

HEALTH CHALLENGE

Select a household chore which Mom or Dad usually does at home to do for a week. It may be as simple as bringing in the laundry or putting out the garbage. You'll be surprised how much they will appreciate it!

BALANCING YOUR LIFESTYLE

Indicators

- Identifies various aspects of his/her life.
- Identifies areas of his/her lifestyle which may need changing.

Teacher information

- Students read the information text at the top of the page.
- To complete the table, students need to fill in the time spent doing homework, sleeping, eating and drinking. For the areas such as relaxation, socializing, and sports and leisure, students may need to list individual activities under these headings and add the times together to give a total.

Additional activities

- Students list healthy and unhealthy foods consumed over a given time period to see how healthy their diet is and what changes need to be made. They could repeat the activity and compare active and sedentary activities done during a given time period to see changes which could be made.
- Students use a pie graph to record the time spent each day doing each type of activity.
- Students interview their parents to see what changes they would like to make to be more healthy and fit.

Answers

Answers will vary

SELF-MANAGEMENT

www.worldteacherspress.com ©World Teachers Press®

Balancing Your Lifestyle

A person who has a balanced life tries to eat healthy food, gets regular exercise, enjoys some relaxation as well as work or school, and gets enough sleep to cope with the physical demands of daily life.

1. Complete the table below showing the amount of time spent on each activity over one week. Where space has been provided, list the various types of relaxation, socializing, and sports and leisure activities done.

Activity	Total time taken
Homework	
Sleep	
Relaxation	
Eating and drinking	
Socializing	
Sports/leisure	

2. Complete the sentences.
   (a)   I spend the most time doing _____ activities.
   (b)   I spend the least amount of time doing _____ activities.

3. To have a balanced lifestyle,
   (a)   I need to spend more time

   (b)   I need to spend less time

4. My lifestyle is balanced.

   | YES | NO |

   HEALTH CHALLENGE

   Select one of your answers to Question 3 and carry it out for one week.

DON'T WORRY! BE HAPPY!

SELF-MANAGEMENT

Indicators

- Reads information about stress.
- Completes a table using information about stress.

Teacher information

- The process of growing up can be stressful for children. The pace of life is faster and changes occur rapidly. Children are expected to perform better at school and cope with all other aspects of life, often without having any idea of strategies to deal with stress. Situations beyond the control of children will often cause them stress. These include death, divorce, family health problems, parental and school demands, peer pressure, media influences and others. Stress can affect the emotional, social and academic areas of a child's life.

- Research has shown that these factors make children able to manage stress: good self-esteem, a sense of humor, some measure of control over their lives, good parental support with consistent rules at home, good communication within the family, and good relationships with friends and teachers. They may also have some religious affiliation and are recognized for their achievements.

- A certain amount of stress can often have a positive effect on people. Stress may encourage students and adults to improve their performance because it increases energy levels and causes a faster reaction time. Too much stress, however, is harmful as it causes physical, mental, emotional and behavioral problems.

- Read and discuss the information text with the students before they complete the table independently.

- Answers can be discussed and additional information added to each column in the table.

Additional activities

- Students role-play various body signals which show stress.
- Students suggest various stressful situations and role-play ways to cope with them.
- Students form pairs or small groups to create STRESS LESS cards. They can think of unusual or humorous ways to ways to cope with stressful situations. Groups or pairs can share their cards with the class.

Answers

Teacher check

Don't Worry! Be Happy!

- *Everyone experiences stress at some time or other. Life can be very hectic and this may cause worries. Many children have to deal with broken families, moving, changing schools, pressure from friends and family, school demands, death or sickness in the family, and changes to their bodies. Learning strategies to deal with stress can prevent physical problems from developing into severe illnesses. Even adults may attend stress management courses to learn ways to cope with the increasing demands of daily life!*

- *How do you know when you are feeling "stressed out"? A person who is feeling stressed may show signs such as a tight throat, sweaty palms, headaches, fatigue, nausea, diarrhea, uneasiness, depression, restlessness, frustration, or a change in sleeping patterns. Other symptoms include withdrawal, irritability, aggression, excessive daydreaming, excessive sensitivity, changing eating habits and changes in behavior.*

- *In order to cope with stress, there are a number of strategies which may help. These include eating a balanced diet and getting some form of physical exercise. A fit and healthy person is better able to deal with stress, and exercise can provide a physical outlet for stressful feelings. Other strategies include: getting enough sleep or rest, learning relaxation skills, learning to cope with criticism, having a routine to follow, viewing stressful situations in more positive ways, developing problem-solving skills, learning time-management skills, becoming more assertive, developing a sense of humor, or sharing worries with a friend or family member. Even getting a hug from Mom or Dad may help!*

1. Complete the table with keywords and phrases from the text. You may add some more information of your own if you wish.

Causes of stress	Signs of stress	Strategies to deal with stress

HEALTH CHALLENGE

Think about a friend who may be showing signs of stress. Think of one thing you could do to help that person to "stress less." It may be something as simple as lending a sympathetic ear or telling a joke.

HOW DO YOU COPE WITH STRESS?

SELF-MANAGEMENT

Indicators

- Identifies situations which cause him/her stress.
- Identifies personal symptoms of stress.
- Identifies strategies to deal with stress.

Teacher information

- Many students may not be aware that they actually use strategies for dealing with stress, and some may be introduced to new ways of dealing with stressful situations by reading the information on page 67.

- Often, adults and children cope with stress by eating. This is called "emotional eating" and can lead to an excessive food intake. Students will become aware that many people use eating as a way to cope with stress. Students need to find more constructive methods of dealing with stress. Teachers may need to rethink strategies for rewarding good work done by students by not giving food rewards too often. Other rewards, such as extra free-time reading, could be used instead.

- Students can discuss Question 1 with a friend before completing the answers.

- Students can write the answers to Questions 2 , 3 and 4 independently.

NOTE: Some students may not feel comfortable talking about situations which are stressful, such as bullying or having to cope with a new stepparent. Sensitivity should be shown to these students and their problems.

Additional activities

- Students discuss and list different strategies for dealing with the same situation.

- Students create colorful posters using keywords for coping with stress; e.g., "relax," "exercise," "take ten deep breaths," "talk to a friend," "hug a tree."

- Allow students to spend a short time each day at school listening to relaxing music. This may be during silent reading time, before or after breaks. (Students may discuss the best music for this purpose.)

Answers

Teacher check

How Do You Cope with Stress?

Stress is a normal part of life for everyone. Learning to identify symptoms of stress and learning strategies to cope with stress are essential skills in life.

1. List and describe two stressful situations with which you may have had to cope.

    Situation 1   Situation 2

2. Using the information on page 67, write a list of symptoms which you may have experienced in stressful situations. You may add extra information of your own.

3. List any strategies which you may have used to cope with a stressful situation.

    _____

    _____

    _____

    _____

    _____

    _____

4. Select a strategy which you have not used before but would like to try.

    _____

    _____

    _____

    _____

HEALTH CHALLENGE

Use the new strategy you selected in Question 4 and try it to see if it works!

BODY IMAGE

Indicators

- Learns about body image.
- Identifies factors which affect body image.

Teacher information

- Children are influenced by parental and teacher attitudes. If an adult puts a lot of emphasis on appearance and dieting, then so will the child.
- An individual's identity is not determined solely by his/her appearance but also by aspects such as personality, skills, talents and attitude towards life. Emphasis should be given to these aspects of each individual to develop positive self-esteem.
- Read and discuss the information text with the students. They can then complete the questions in pairs.

Additional activities

- Students write poems about feeling good about themselves.
- Discuss well-known television personalities who have had plastic surgery. What are the reasons for doing this? What are the advantages and disadvantages of having plastic surgery? Discuss plastic surgery done for reasons such as severe disfigurements and life-threatening conditions.
- Construct a "perfect" person. Cut pictures of people from magazines who students consider to be "perfect." Cut and glue together different body parts from different personalities and view the finished products. Why do students have different ideas about what they consider to be a "perfect" person?

Answers

Teacher check

SELF-MANAGEMENT

Body Image

Body image means how you see, think and feel about your body. This usually has very little to do with how you actually look!

Many people worry about how they look and what others think about how they look. Having a poor body image can lead to abnormal behaviors, such as excessive dieting and exercising or binge eating.

There are two main reasons why we look the way we do.

*The most important reason is **genetics**. This means that we inherit characteristics from our parents, grandparents, aunts and uncles and other members of our family. There is very little we can do about this except make the best of what we have been given.*

*The second reason is **how well you look after yourself**. You will look and feel better about yourself if you:*

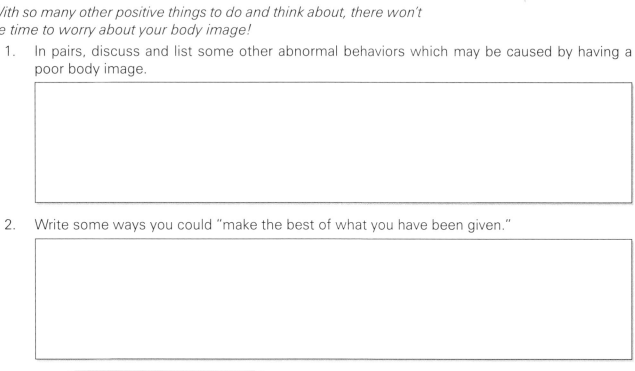

- *eat healthy food*
- *drink plenty of water*
- *exercise to keep your body looking the best it can*
- *get enough sleep or rest*
- *find time to relax and have fun*
- *work and keep active*
- *share with and care about other people*
- *keep away from unhealthy environments such as those where there is cigarette smoke*

With so many other positive things to do and think about, there won't be time to worry about your body image!

1. In pairs, discuss and list some other abnormal behaviors which may be caused by having a poor body image.

2. Write some ways you could "make the best of what you have been given."

HEALTH CHALLENGE

With a friend, write a list of things you like about yourselves. You are not allowed to include anything you don't like!

BODY SMART

Indicator

- Completes information about body image.

Teacher information

- We are constantly bombarded with images in the media about how we should look. If we don't look like the images on television or in magazines, then we may start to feel that we are not as good as everyone else. Very few people have flawless features and perfect bodies. This inability to meet the standards set by others may lead to low self-esteem.

- Other people we come into contact with may also influence our opinion of ourselves with positive and negative comments.

- Some strategies which help with positive body image include:

  – Think positively—focus on the things that you like about yourself.

  – Associate with people who have a healthy attitude towards food, weight and body image.

  – Eat healthy food. Aim to be as healthy as possible and you will look better on the outside as well as feel better on the inside.

  – Be as active as you can. Find some exercise which you enjoy doing and start doing it. Exercising makes you feel better about your body, helps you to relax or relieve stress, and gives you more energy.

- Read and discuss the information text with the students. They can then select two classmates to collect information from in order to complete the table.

Note: Shy students or those with a poor body image may not wish to share their answers to some questions on this worksheet with others. Consideration for their feelings should be shown.

Additional activities

- Students discuss and list sports and television personalities they admire because of their skills, talents and personality.

- Discuss the health risks of getting skin cancer in the quest for a tanned body.

- List strategies for developing positive body images, such as saying one positive thing to himself/herself each day.

Answers

Teacher check

Body Smart

We all come from different family backgrounds. This means that we are supposed to look different too! Even people within one family, although sharing the same genes, look different from each other. Our world would be very boring if we all looked the same!

An individual's appearance is also influenced by other factors—personality, attitudes, talents and skills—not just physical appearance.

1. Select two of your friends. Use information about them to complete the table below.

Friend 1 _____	Friend 2 _____
Appearance	Appearance
Personality	Personality
Skills	Skills
Talents	Talents
What I like about this person	What I like about this person

From the table above it is easy to see the similarities and differences. We also need to realize that no one is perfect! However, we can all make the best of what we have been given and feel good about ourselves!

2. Use the box to complete information about yourself.

Appearance	Skills/Talents
Personality	What I like about myself

HEALTH CHALLENGE

Choose a student in your class to whom you don't often speak. Think of one compliment to give to that person about his/her appearance, personality, skills, or talents. Choose a different student each week!

MAKING CHOICES

SELF-MANAGEMENT

Indicators

- Reads information about making choices.
- Shows understanding of the influences on individual choices.

Teacher information

- Decisions for young children are most often made by their parents. As children get older, they begin to make more choices for themselves. They also need to take responsibility for the decisions they make, whether they have positive or negative consequences. Some decisions are easy and have little consequence, such as choosing what to eat for breakfast. Others are more difficult, and decisions regarding these need to be planned.

- A simple plan when making decisions follows the steps below:
  - Decide what the problem is
  - Decide what the choices are
  - Think of all the consequences of the choices
  - Select the best choice based on the information gained from the previous steps

- Students read and discuss the text, then complete the table and sentence.

Additional activities

- Record one or two commercials on TV shown during children's viewing time. Play them to the students and critically analyze them. Discuss advertising techniques used to encourage viewers to buy the product.

- Survey students to discover how many have bought the same product which they saw advertised on television. Discuss reasons for selecting the products.

- Students create an advertisement for a popular magazine to persuade readers to buy a particular product.

Answers

Teacher check

Making Choices

People spend many hours watching television each day as well as reading magazines and newspapers. The media can have a great influence on various decisions we need to make. The media tells us the way we should look, what we should eat, how we should behave and what we should wear. As we become more aware of how advertising works, we can also become more critical of advertising and able to make informed decisions for ourselves.

Other influences on decisions we make include parents, friends and celebrities. Who or what influences your choices?

1. Complete the survey below by checking the appropriate boxes. In the last box, give an example if possible.

What	Choice influenced by ...				Example
	Media	Parent(s)	Friends	Celebrities	
snack foods eaten					
clothes bought and worn					
books read					
computer games bought and used					
DVDs bought or watched					
CDs bought or listened to					
takeout meals eaten					
exercise choices					

2. Count the number of checks in each column and complete the sentence.

   "I am most influenced by _____"

HEALTH CHALLENGE

Be a critical viewer of advertisements! Think about whether the ad is truthful and what the advertisers are doing to make you want to buy the product. Do you really like the product, or do you want it because everyone else has it?

PEERS AND CHOICES

Indicator

- Reads and answers questions about the influence of peers upon choices.

Teacher information

- Children often make decisions based on whether or not it will help them fit into their particular group. They make decisions which they know are wrong in order to achieve this goal. Children need to develop enough confidence to say "no" if a decision is harmful to themselves or others.

- Read and discuss the introductory text at the top of the page with the students.

- Allow the students time to read each scenario in Question 1 and complete the columns. Specific scenarios may be discussed if desired.

- Students read the text and complete Question 2 in small groups. Groups report to the class. Students may discuss specific situations if needed.

Additional activities

- Students discuss situations relating to diet and exercise where peers may influence their choices, such as consuming snack foods, drinks and fast foods.

- Students write a short text to encourage peers to attempt a new activity which will be beneficial to them. This may include activities such as a physical game, sports, or leisure activity.

- Students relate situations where choices are difficult to make and compromises may need to be made, or where more than one choice is acceptable; for example, scenario 1 (c).

Answers

Teacher check

SELF-MANAGEMENT

Peers and Choices

The sense of belonging, or being part of a group, is important to everyone. We like to be part of a group and to be liked by them. This gives peers some degree of power over each other. Because we want to belong and to be accepted by peers, we are more willing to do and say things and act like them.

Peer influence can be positive or negative. Peers can encourage us to do our best or pressure us to do things that we know are wrong.

We are all different individuals, so we cannot expect to think, act, or be the same.

1. Read each scenario below. Next to each, say whether the peer pressure is a positive or negative and decide the correct action to take in each situation, explaining why.

	Scenario	Positive/ Negative	Correct action to take and reason
(a)	Emily and Natasha are buying some milk and a newspaper at the local delicatessen for Emily's mom. Natasha asks Emily to keep the store clerk busy while she takes a bottle of soda.		Emily should:
(b)	Brian is a good runner. He enters the cross country run at school. He really wants his friend, David, to compete because he is a fast runner too. David is shy and doesn't like being the center of attention, but Brian tries to persuade him to compete too.		Brian should:
(c)	Tess and her friends are going to the school dance. Her friends have decided to all wear the same color and type of clothes. Tess's mom bought her a really gorgeous outfit last weekend, and she really wants to wear it.		Tess should:
(d)	Warren and Rhyce are going to the water park with their mom and dad. They have invited their friend, Nigel, to come. Nigel has never been before, so he doesn't know what to expect.		Nigel should:

Peers can help make choices easier. They can give you information to help you make more informed, clearer choices. The final choice is always up to you!

2. In small groups, make a list of occasions when it has been helpful to discuss something with a friend before making a decision. Say whether the discussion influenced or confirmed your own decision. Report back to the class.

HEALTH CHALLENGE

Friends can introduce you to new experiences. An activity which may be new and scary may be easier to experience if you take a friend with you. Make sure that it is a safe, fun activity and have a try!!

GOAL–SETTING

Indicator

- Reads information and answers questions about goal setting.

Teacher information

- Goals should be something that a person really wants and not something that just "sounds good." A constructive goal motivates a person to achieve the set goal and makes it a worthwhile experience.

- Setting goals in each area of life ensures a more balanced life, because existing structures are examined and changed. It also helps to eliminate unimportant aspects.

- Goals should be a positive thing. Thinking positively gives one a brighter outlook on life.

- Goals should be detailed. For example, instead of having a goal which says "I will be healthier" it would be better to choose specific goals such as "I will cut all cakes and cookies from my diet."

- Set a goal which is high. Even if you do not reach this goal, you may find yourself at a better place in your life, having achieved some important steps along the way.

- Goals should be specific, measurable, challenging, realistic and have a completion date.

- Read and discuss the information text with the students. They can then complete the questions individually. Some students may not wish to share answers with the class if they have a very personal goal.

Additional activities

- Read biographies about people who have achieved remarkable goals.

- Invite a local sports, media, or civic personality to speak to the class about working towards a goal.

- Students write a "Goals for my life" list. Date and, enclose in a decorated cylinder. Take it home for safekeeping. Label it with the words "Do not open until 2025."

Answers

Teacher check

Goal-Setting

Goal: something towards which effort is directed in order to achieve; an aim or end.

People who set goals experience success. In order to achieve goals, strategies and specific steps need to be formulated. Goals need to be clear and have a specific plan of action.

Goals must:

- *be specific.*
- *have a time line for achieving.*
- *be planned and have organized strategies.*
- *be achievable.*
- *be able to be controlled.*
- *have specific steps.*

People who set a goal must be accountable for their own progress towards their goal.

Answer these questions.

1. In your own words, explain what you think a goal is and how to achieve it.

_____

_____

_____

_____

_____

2. Give an example of a goal you set for yourself and tell how you achieved it.

_____

_____

_____

_____

_____

_____

3. Complete the boxes below to show how to achieve a new goal. Use the information at the top of the page to help.

Target date	This goal is important because ...	Steps to achieve my goal

Difficulties which may occur	Goal	

I will know I have achieved my goal when ...

HEALTH CHALLENGE

Choose a healthy lifestyle goal such as trying to eat more healthy food and compile steps to achieve it.

HEALTHY CHOICES

TIME MANAGEMENT AND GOALS

Indicators

- Reads information about managing time in order to achieve goals.
- Identifies goals and formulates plans to carry them out.

Teacher information

- Ensure students understand the steps to follow to complete Question 1.
- Students should select specific goals for Question 2, such as trying to eat five servings of vegetables and two fruits each day, and drinking more water daily.

Additional activities

- Students complete a food and exercise diary for a week. At the end of the week, they evaluate whether they have achieved their goal or not.
- Students keep a diary of time spent watching television or using the computer. Using this information, students allocate their time each day so they are not spending more than two hours each day doing these activities. Prioritizing television programs in order from most to least favorite will help students to fit in the ones they like best. It will also show them which television shows they watch just because the television is on.
- Students brainstorm to list rewards (other than food) to give and receive upon achieving a goal. The list may include such things as free time, sleepovers with friends, a CD to dance to and sing with, or a family outing to a special place.

Answers

Teacher check

Time Management and Goals

In order to achieve a more balanced, healthy lifestyle, it is important to manage your time well to achieve the goals you have set for yourself.

1. Your goal is to try to be more active each week, so that in six months' time you will be fitter and healthier. Use the timetable below to show when and how you could add more activity to your week. Don't forget that doing more active things does not always mean going for a jog or doing weight-lifting at the gym. It may be as simple as helping to take the dog for a walk or cleaning the car for Mom or Dad. Include any activities which you already do.

Day/Date	Activity	Time spent
Monday _____		
Tuesday _____		
Wednesday _____		
Thursday _____		
Friday _____		
Saturday _____		
Sunday _____		

2. Use the format below to write a healthy food goal.

My goal is _____

The steps to reach my goal are _____

_____

_____

I will reach my goal on _____

HEALTH CHALLENGE

Start a food and exercise diary to record what you are eating and how much exercise you are doing each day!